NEW CENTURY READERS

Myths and Legends

A Selection of Short Stories

Edited by Paul Francis and Gill Murray

Edinburgh Gate
Harlow, Essex

Pearson Education Limited
Edinburgh Gate
Harlow
Essex
CM20 2JE
England

First published in Great Britain by Pearson Education 2003

This edition first published by Pearson Education 2003
Editorial notes © Pearson Education Limited 2003

Third impression 2005
ISBN: 0582 42943 9

Printed in China
GCC/03

The Publisher's policy is to use paper manufactured from sustainable
forests

Editorial notes by Paul Francis and Gill Murray
Designed and packaged by McLean Press Ltd
Cover illustration by Charlotte Combe

Contents

Tell Me That Again

Introduction

Setting the scene

We have put together this collection to provide a number of stories which we hope you will enjoy. They vary – they're long and short, from different countries, and they're written in different ways. That variety is part of the enjoyment.

These are stories that have been told for a long time, all over the world. People used to think that because they were told to children, there was something childish about them. They called them fairystories, and tried to make them harmless. But these stories are not safe. They are powerful, and people of all ages are affected by them. They stay with us and we know them, even if we sometimes think that we don't. Adult writers, painters and musicians still spend years exploring them, working out what they mean.

Each story in this book was written down, on paper, by one person. They've chosen their words, and thought about how the story should be told. But they haven't made them up. They've taken them on, from other books, and other storytellers, and the stories began when there were no books. People sat around fires and passed on stories, for many different reasons.

In this book there are clear links, where two stories in a section are like each other, or do the same thing in different ways. But there are other links, across sections as well as within them, where stories connect with each other, and one story makes you think of another one. You need to look out for these, and find good ways of exploring them.

It's hard to say where myths begin and end. There are stories here which have lasted for hundreds of years, and will never be lost. But people work on them, tell them in different ways, and try to bring them alive. We have always thought about the big ideas, love and money, birth and death, but there are also new stories, about hitchhikers and commuters, internet lovers and winners of the lottery.

You will know many stories, not just from printed books but from picture books and poems, comics and films. And you will find that many of them are like the stories in this book, because myths and legends stay with us. If we read them, think about them, and tell them again, then we give them a life of their own.

Main themes and characters

We've arranged these stories into four groups, because it can make it interesting to put stories together. We see how the same idea can be explored in different countries, or the various ways people talk about discovering fire, being poor or falling in love.

What Makes a Story Last?

The first group of stories looks at the power of the story – why we keep reading. It might be because we want to see what happens next; will Persephone escape from hell? Will Beowulf kill the monster? Or maybe we put ourselves in the place of the main person – what would I do, if my dad wanted to marry me?

Underdogs can win. Sometimes the poor girl (in *The Invisible One*) or the struggling farmer (in *What Are Friends For?*) can come out on top. Despite appearances at the beginning of the story, they can end up successful, powerful or in love. And for people who are not rich or powerful, who seem likely to end up losing, that can be a really good story to tell.

What Does a Story Mean?

The Greek storyteller Aesop wrote Fables, which would end up with lines like 'MORAL: Look before you leap'. Not many stories teach lessons as simply as that, but they do have meanings. We are meant to enjoy them, to follow the telling and see what happens next. But we're also meant to think about them afterwards.

Some stories explain how the earth was made, or why we have spring and winter. Some were about the discovery of fire, or how things were made – whether they are mountains or squirrels (like *How Coyote Stole Fire*). And some are about what sort of people we are, and how we are meant to behave. What happens to us, and to other people, if we're selfish, (like *The Wicked King and his Good Son*) or in love (like *Deer Hunter and White Corn Maiden*)?

But these stories don't have a moral tacked on to them, and we might have got them wrong. Other people might read the same stories, and come up with different meanings. So you have to read them, and find out what you think they are about. That's part of the fun, the reason why we read stories and keep telling them – so that we can work out for ourselves what we think they mean.

The Way You Tell Them
A joke is a joke, but the same joke can sound different, depending on the way it's told. The same applies to stories. It's partly what happens, and the people in it, and what it might possibly mean. But it's also the way it's told. In this section we look at techniques of storytelling, things you might do which would help you to tell a story well.

Some stories sound as if a god was telling them, handing them down from above (*Balder*, for example). Others sound like a man in a pub, or a rap performer (as in *The Mind of Anansi*). As you read, you need to work out who the storyteller is, and how they know what they tell. How do they feel about it, and how should we react? The way a storyteller speaks to us is vital: what is their tone of voice? It's useful to think of words for this – relaxed, excited, solemn, chatty and so on. (Find some more of your own.)

With tone, there's also rhythm. These are both words we use

about poetry, and that's right, because stories, like poems, are meant to be heard as well as read. Sometimes you need to get the sound of a story to know what's going on. *Balder, The Death of Gelert* and *The Mind of Anansi* each use rhythm to get across the feeling of the story, but it's a different rhythm in each case.

There are patterns. There were three sisters … on the way he met three animals … you have three wishes. For people listening, who can't go back and look at earlier bits of the story, this makes it easier to grasp. 'Right,' they say to themselves, ' this is wish number one. Then there'll be two, but the one that matters is three …'.

Stories should be interesting all the way through, but at key moments there should be suspense, when the listener asks what will happen now? Will it be *x* or *y*?

And then there's the ending. What are you left with, when it's over? How did you feel? What is your last impression of the story, and the person who told it? Are they laughing, sad, or shaking their head?

Tell Me That Again
In this section we look at retelling, where modern writers take an old story and write their version of it. The outline of the story, the 'what happens' bit, is fixed, but they still have to answer a number of questions. Who is the storyteller? A god-like figure, up there, telling us what went on? Or close to the action, saying what happens as they see it? Or one of the characters in the story, like Icarus, telling it from his own point of view?

Who is the audience? *The Prometheus Incident* describes violent events in calm, official language. *Little Red Riding Hood: The Wolf's Story* takes a story we all know, but turns it round: it's American not English, it's from the wolf's point of view, not Red Riding Hood's – so what difference does that make?

Some stories make people angry, so they change them, turn them back upon themselves. Some people retell stories they love, to bring out what they like about them, or what they think is still relevant and up to date. Always there are choices, different ways of doing things. Which bits of the story will they pick? What sort of language will they use? How does it change a story, to tell it as a poem? The point is not to choose the best, pick one rather than another, but to see how many possibilities there are. 'If I tackled this story, I might do that with it, or that, or ...'. Have fun.

What Makes a Story Last?

Notes on Persephone in Hell

The ancient Greeks believed not in one god but in many and they told dramatic and often violent stories about their feuds and struggles for power. You can find other versions of the Persephone story told by the Romans (Ceres and Proserpina) and there is a much older Babylonian version (Ishtar and Tammuz).

The Greeks imagined that each god had particular responsibilities. Zeus was the chief god and ruled from Mount Olympus. Apollo was the sun god, Artemis the moon goddess. Poseidon ruled the seas and Demeter the land and all that grew there. When people died, they believed their spirits went to an underworld ruled over by Hades, Zeus' brother. Before this story begins Demeter's daughter has been captured by Hades and taken down to his gloomy kingdom. Demeter is wild with grief and this has terrible effects on the natural world.

What do you think?
Look carefully at the opening and discuss the different kinds of damage that Demeter threatens to cause.

The main players in this drama are: Zeus; Demeter; Persephone; Hades; Hermes and Ascalaphus.

As you read, think about what motivates each of these. Is it easy to decide where your sympathies lie?

Questions
1. Why does Demeter feel that Hades' kingdom will be a terrible place for her daughter?
2. Zeus has the power to order his brother to release Persephone but he makes one important condition. What is this? Can you think why he chose it?
3. Hades' kingdom is as deep and dark as Olympus is high and bright. Which words or phrases has the writer used to create a vivid picture of the underworld?
4. Why does Hades eventually agree to allow Persephone to return to earth? Why does this not go according to plan?
5. Who are the winners and losers in this story?

8

Persephone in Hell

Persephone, the goddess of spring, has been taken by Hades down to hell. Her mother Demeter, goddess of the earth, asks Zeus, the king of the gods, to get her daughter back.

Wild of aspect and terrible in her anguish, the great goddess stood before her greater brother on the rocky steeps of high Olympus. The clouds trembled and the stars crept frightened into their holes as Demeter cursed the sky that had looked down on the rape of her child by Hades, hateful god of the dead.

'Nor will I bless the earth again, brother, till Persephone returns. All will die, mighty Zeus. The rich wide garden will shrivel and crack till Hades inherits it all. Apollo and Artemis will shine on slowly-turning emptiness and death. The bright nymphs and earth-spirits will fly into the void and be lost in eternity. Even Poseidon will raise his trident against you. In all the universe only grim Hades will stretch out his dark hand towards you. I swear it, brother. I swear it by the River Styx.'

The lord of the sky shuddered and his golden brow grew heavy as Demeter took the oath that none of the gods might break.

'Hades is a great god,' said Zeus at length, staring down on the bleak, leafless trees and the blind, grey earth. 'It is no little thing, sister, for our child to be his queen.'

'What has young Persephone to do with that grim king?' raged Demeter. 'What flowers are there in his cold

9

fields; what sun, what air, what light? She loved music, great Zeus. Now she must hear the groans of the damned and the sighs of the forgotten. Is that to be her wedding hymn? She loved the fruits of the earth: what is there now for her wedding feast but the dust of bones?'

Hot tears ran down Demeter's cheeks and dropped scalding on, the mountain rock. All her immortal beauty was grown stony with misery; even her rich breasts – between which Zeus himself had once laid his head – seemed dry and cold as marble.

Persephone – Persephone!' she wept. 'If you are lost to me for ever, what do I care if the universe dies?'

The father of the gods stared at the tragic goddess and brooded on the calamity of her oath. His gigantic mind stretched itself till it encompassed all teeming creation, reaching into the farthest crannies where secret creatures thought themselves forgotten and unwatched. Then he weighed the tiniest cry against the loudest uproar of storms … for everything had its place.

He called for Hermes, his messenger.

'Go,' commanded Zeus. 'Go to my brother Hades and bid him free Persephone. It is my decree. But – ' The lord of the sky frowned as the bright messenger trembled on the air. 'But if she has tasted of the food of the dead, then she must remain in darkness forever. This is the decree of the Fates.'

He turned to the goddess whose eyes were radiant. 'You have angered them, sister; and they have their powers. Go, Hermes – to the kingdom of the dead.'

The air grew briefly fiery; the clouds parted – then drifted slowly down the gleaming funnel made by the messenger's flight, till the print of his staff, his outstretched arms and the curious wings of his sandals, dreamed and rolled away. ...

Hermes took the path that Zeus and his brothers had taken long ago, when they'd freed the ancient prisoners of Tartarus. This was through the grove of black poplars that grew by the ocean. He sped high over the quiet River Styx, flickering in the thick air so that Charon, the fleshless boatman, looked up and wondered at a star so far from the sky. Then, on the farther bank, Cerberus, dread hound of hell, raised its three huge heads, swaying them hither and thither so that its fierce eyes seemed to smear the night with blood.

The god flew on, now over the grey spotted Fields of Asphodel where the vague dead rustled like dry, invisible leaves. Beyond, like two tarnished mirrors, lay the pools of Memory and Forgetfulness, partly overhung by thin white trees which nodded as they dropped their bitter berries. ...

Multitudinous ghosts clustered about them, moving desolately from one to the other as they sought to quench pain with pain.

The messenger shuddered at the scope of the dark kingdom whose gloomy plains stretched to eternal loneliness. He thought of bright Persephone moving across them – and he sped fast and faster yet till he came at last to the palace of Hades, grim counterpart of high Olympus.

Black and huge it stood before him, wrapped in a brooding silence.

The ranked pillars of towering jet that guarded the portico suddenly gleamed with tall streaks of silver as the god passed between them. Then they sank into their old blackness: the god was within.

Down endless corridors Hermes flickered, turning this way and that as sudden walls menaced him with his own shadow and turned his staff into a weapon of snakes.

Deeper and deeper he pierced into the labyrinth, till the darkness began to burn and glow and the carved cornices were painted with wrinkled gold.

Little by little the glow grew stronger as the god sped on towards the source of it. Little by little it turned the paved floor into a brazen river that ran between dark golden trees reaching up to a crazed and cracked golden sky from which blind carbuncles, opals and dim grey diamonds stared down like a universe of dead stars.

Such were the riches of Hades, lord of the dead.

'What do you want with me?'

Immortal Hermes had entered the presence of the god.

Vast Hades, crouching on his heavy throne, scowled down at the sleek bright messenger from distant Olympus.

'Yours is a rich kingdom, uncle,' said Hermes, glancing courteously round at the endless, brooding gold.

'Mine is a lonely kingdom,' said the god harshly.

'Indeed?' The god of thieves, drawing designs on the. engraved floor with his staff, looked up. 'I understand that it is not so lonely as it used to be.'

Hades' scowl deepened. Savage fires seemed to spring up in the caverns of his eyes.

'The Lady Persephone,' went on Zeus's messenger, staring now at the crusted roof, now at the rich carvings that swelled and twisted from the walls till they seemed to drip in a slow metallic torrent. 'Great Demeter's child.'

'What do you want? Speak plain; for once.'

But Hermes was not given to plain speech. He smiled and flickered to the side of the dreadful throne, even overhanging it. ...

'Between you and me, uncle, I understand she is not happy here. They say she grows thin and pale and spends her time in weeping. She will not eat with you ... Though it's no affair of mine, Lord Hades, I fancy some nymph or goddess of a more yielding nature than Demeter's child would make a more agreeable queen.'

'Is that the message from my great brother?'

Immortal Hermes sighed, and put away tact. 'My father bids you free Persephone, Lord Hades.'

'No ... no ...'

The god's whisper seemed to fill his terrible palace so that all its dead substance whispered with him. 'No ... no ...'

Then Hermes raised his herald's staff and reminded the huge, crouching Hades that he, like all creation, was subject to the thunderbolt. Hades raised his eyes. There was bleak hatred in them; and a grief as wild and savage as Demeter's.

'Persephone. ...'

Once more the brazen labyrinth echoed with the god's whisper, till it seemed to waiting Hermes that all the kingdom of the dead was muttering, 'Persephone ...Persephone. ...'

Then she came. The layered air began to move as vague warmth stole upon it. The cracked columns that stood at the chamber's entrance like an iron forest began to wink and gleam as if to a wandering sunrise in a flowered gown.

'Persephone!'

The child of Zeus and Demeter stood before the dark throne.

She swayed slightly and touched at a rent in the shoulder of her gown. Then she raised her bright, sad eyes and stared at her terrible lover while her radiance softly flooded the room. The gold began to gleam and shine and the vaulted ceiling blushed into a sky of jewels that danced in the light. The dull chamber seemed changed into a marvellous casket, most intricately wrought. It was full of nymphs and Tritons and ferns and strange stories told in the devious walls.

'Persephone!'

Hermes marvelled and understood why grim Hades had dared to challenge the power of Olympus.

She had come from the gardens that stretched beyond the palace ... and a withered, white-haired creature had followed her in. He was a gardener and his name was Ascalaphus. Painfully he watched her, with eyes like a pair of blasted moons,

His arms, long and sinewy from reaching up to prune the black, quiet trees, now hung down and his thin fingers were spread as if everywhere in the young goddess's wake he found the ghosts of flowers.

'Since I cannot make you happy, Persephone, you must return.' Hades' words came slow and gratingly, as if they were being forced from cracking iron.

Demeter's child looked unbelievingly at the huge dark god. Her lips parted in the amazement of her joy.

'I loved you, Persephone,' whispered Hades. 'But that was not enough.' Tears as red as blood were coursing down his shadowy cheeks.

'Go! Go!' he shouted suddenly; and his voice sent the brazen echoes rolling down the corridors till the columns trembled and the walls shook.

'You'll not regret this, uncle,' murmured Hermes hastily and began to draw bright Persephone back from the throne and towards the pillared entrance of the chamber. All creation will applaud your wise and generous act.'

But the god, watching the sweet light go, groaned only, 'Persephone … Persephone. …'

Already she was among the iron trees and tile eternal chamber of Hades was sinking into its gigantic, gilded gloom. The bright stars died and the stories in the walls ended in the weight of hanging nightmare.

'The gods will honour you,' came Hermes' dwindling

voice winding back among the pillars, 'and even the hard Fates will nod their heads, uncle. For this is their wish, too. Persephone must return, they decreed, if she has eaten no food of the dead.'

No food of the·dead. … The herald's voice seemed to ripple among the columns like a tide receding.

'*No food of the dead*?'

Ascalaphus, the hideous gardener, awoke from his withered dream with a shriek. He began to choke and cough and shout with malignant laughter.

'Seven seeds!' he screeched. 'She ate seven seeds! I saw her! Pomegranate seeds – red as her blood!'

The dreadful creature was capering up and down in triumph and waving his arms like shabby wings. 'Now she must stay! Now she must walk *my* gardens and gather *my* flowers for ever!'

They met at Eleusis; the goddess and her lost child. And though the frantic joy of their meeting seemed to make a little summer in the midst of the stricken land, it was only at Eleusis. Such joy as this could neither spread nor endure. Its substance was tears; its purpose – farewell. Persephone was for the kingdom of Hades; Demeter was for the eternal winter of the world.

'The Fates! The Fates!' screeched the hellish gardener, whose tongue had damned Demeter and her child. He clung to the rim of the great goddess's chariot-wheel as if to prevent its escape. Dead, bent and dusty, he blinked enviously in the light of day.

'I was the instrument of the Fates!'

'Then be forever hated,' cursed wild Demeter, 'like the malignant hags themselves!'

She raised her hand and struck him across the mouth. At once, that venomous thing split and gaped. The skin shrivelled, and hardened into beaked bone. Then the face about it shrank and darkened till the bright, spiteful eyes all but engulfed it. His long arms, beating and flailing against horrible pain, bent and cracked and splintered into changed shapes – and the flesh was torn into feathers. He shrieked and screamed – but no longer in words.

'Foul creature, begone!'

At the goddess's command, it rose, still screaming, from her chariot-wheel and beat raggedly away to hide itself forever in those gnawed-off scraps of hell that still littered the world of day. A screech-owl ever doomed to hoot disaster in the midst of joy!

Demeter forsook the company of gods and men. She wept no more, as if she feared her very tears might nourish the world she'd cursed. Haggard and terrible, she broke through the naked forests where the beasts died and the streams froze.

Sometimes she would kneel and gaze down into the thick ice to where the caught nymph or genius of the waters lay staring up, pierced .with needles of broken crystal. Anguish answered anguish, and the goddess moved on.

One by one her sisters and brothers in immortality pleaded with her, but to each and all of them she had given the same reply:

17

'Persephone – Persephone! Give me back my child!'

At last she trailed her desolate gown back into Attica. She wandered across the barren lap of Mount Hymettus where the wild bees used to make honey for the gods. The once fair garden of ancient Prometheus crumbled under her feet. Suddenly, she stumbled and cried out in pain. A potsherd had cut her heel. She bent to pick it up. Was it from the very jar in which the Titan had kept the substance he had fashioned into man? Demeter shook her head. What did it matter now? All labour was in vain. ...

'Demeter, my child.'

The goddess looked up. Though sinking into ruin, parts of the Titan's house still stood. The voice that called her had come from within.

'Demeter – great goddess of the harvests!'

Slowly, she entered the house. It was cold and rank. Rooms had fallen one into another, and all that remained of the strange chamber where Prometheus had laboured was the withered fig-tree.

'Demeter.' A mighty figure was crouching beside its trunk. It was Rhea, mother of Creation and of Demeter herself.

'Great goddess – you must relent!'

'Give me back my child!'

'I, too, lost children – even you, Demeter.'

'But they returned.'

'Only to be lost again.' Rhea's unfathomed eyes stared at her daughter whose grief was destroying the world. 'Listen,' she whispered. She held up her hand, and

18

Demeter heard from high amid the ragged mountains of the north the screaming of Prometheus in his chains.

'The vulture still flies,' muttered Demeter.

'Not the vulture,' said Rhea, 'but you, my daughter. Prometheus weeps for the world.'

Demeter bowed her head, and sank at her mother's feet.

'Give me back my child.'

Rhea's hand lost itself in the rich gold of her daughter's hair.

'Yes … yes. … She will return, and return again. There will be meetings, Demeter. There will be great broad days of joy. But there must be partings, too. We cannot escape the Fates, my child.'

'Persephone … Persephone! Where are you?'

The bright poppies nodded in the golden field.

'Persephone!'

Then they exploded into a laughing scarlet storm as Persephone, goddess of the spring, flung herself fiercely into Demeter's arms, once more to be armisticed with kisses.

The world was in summer and the days were long. Demeter smiled, all disaster forgotten in her vast nature and love. Then the screech-owl hooted his tale of the pomegranate seeds and the harsh necessity of the Fates. It was time for Demeter and Persephone to part. Three long, dark months must Persephone stay with Hades. Three long, dark months must Demeter wander the world, calling her child in vain. 'Persephone … Persephone. …

But she would come again. Great Rhea had promised. In spite of the Fates, each year Demeter's child would return.

Notes on The Fight with Grendel

This account of a fight with a monster comes from a long poem about a warrior called Beowulf. It began as an oral story, told in Britain but dealing with events in Scandinavia and was first written down, in Old English, or Anglo-Saxon, around AD1000. The epic poem tells of Beowulf's brave deeds but also deals with important issues of life and death, peace and war, the individual and society. As a young warrior Beowulf defends his people against the monster Grendel. (Later in the poem he has to defeat Grendel's even more frightening mother.) If you look at these few lines from the original you will see how much our language has changed in the last thousand years.

ꝥa wæs Hroðgare heresped gyfen,
wiges weorðmynd, ꝥæt him his winemagas
georne hyrdon, oðð ꝥæt seo geogoð geweox,
magodriht micel.

What do you think?
At this time, poets often found different ways of shaping their verse, by paying close attention to the sounds of the words within a line rather than by putting rhymes at the end. In this modern version can you hear any repeated sounds within the lines?

As well as hearing these sound patterns, the original Anglo-Saxon listeners to *Beowulf* would have responded to the strong images created by the poet's words. Notice how Ian Serraillier has also made striking use of language, for instance, describing the Baltic Sea as a 'wintry whale-road'. What other metaphors or similes help you to visualise the settings and action of the story?

Questions
1. Which words or phrases in the first section create the contrast between the world of Heorot and the world of Grendel?
2. Why is Beowulf confident when he first arrives at Heorot that he can help Hrothgar and his people?
3. What warning does Hrothgar have for him?
4. What marks Beowulf out from his fellow warriors as they await the arrival of Grendel?
5. At first Beowulf and Grendel seem evenly matched. Why is Beowulf eventually able to defeat his enemy?

The Fight with Grendel

from Beowulf the Warrior
A modern version by Ian Serraillier

Hrothgar, King of the Danes, glorious in battle,
Built him a huge hall – its gleaming roof
Towering high to heaven – strong to withstand
The buffet of war. He called it Heorot
And lived there with his Queen. At time of feasting
He gave to his followers rings and ornaments
And bracelets of bright gold ...
But away in the treacherous fens, beyond the moor,
A hideous monster lurked, fiend from hell,
Misbegotten son of a foul mother,
Grendel his name, hating the sound of the harp,
The minstrel's song, the bold merriment of men ...
He, one night, when the warriors of Hrothgar lay
Slumbering after banquet, came to Heorot,
Broke down the door, seized in his fell grip
A score and more of the sleeping sons of men
And carried them home for meat. At break of day
The hall of Heorot rang loud and long
With woe of warriors and grief of the great King.
Thereafter, from dark lake and dripping caves
Night after night over the misty moor
Came Grendel, gross and grim, famished for flesh ...
For twelve years he waged war with Hrothgar,
Piling grief upon grief. For twelve years
He haunted great Heorot.

                              Now there lived overseas
In the land of the Geats a youth of valiance abounding,
Mightiest yet mildest of men, his name Beowulf,
Who, hearing of Grendel and minded to destroy him,
Built a boat of the stoutest timber and chose him
Warriors, fourteen of the best. In shining armour
They boarded the great vessel, beached on the shingle
By the curling tide. Straightway they shoved her off.
They ran up the white sail. And the wind caught her,
The biting wind whipped her over the waves.
Like a strong bird the swan-boat winged her way
Over the grey Baltic, the wintry whale-road,
Till the lookout sighted land – a sickle of fair sand
And glittering white cliffs. The keel struck
The shingle. The warriors sprang ashore …

                              Thus came the warriors
To Heorot and, heavy with weariness, halted by the door.
They propped their spears by a pillar; from blistered
    hands
Their shields slid clattering to the floor. Then Wulfgar,
Herald of the King, having demanded their errand,
Ran to his royal master and quick returning
Urged them within. The long hall lay before them,
The floor paved with stone, the roof high-raftered.
In mournful state upon his throne sat brooding
Aged Hrothgar, grey-haired and bowed with grief.
Slowly he raised his eyes, leaden, lustreless,
And gazed upon the youth as with ringing step
Boldly he strode forth till he stood at his feet.

'O noble Hrothgar, giver of treasure,
Lord of the rousing war-song, we bring you greeting.
Because we grieve deep for your desolation,
Over the long paths of the ocean have we laboured,
I and my warriors, to rid you of the brute
That nightly robs you of rest. I am no weakling.
With my trusty blade I have slain a monster brood
And blindly at night many a foul sea-beast
That writhed and twisted in the bounding wave.
I beg you to grant my wish. I shall not fail.'
    Then Hrothgar stretched out his arms in welcome
And took him by the hand and said, 'Beowulf ...
Right gladly I grant your wishes – but first, one word
Of warning. That sword you spoke of – it will avail
Nothing with Grendel, whose life is proof against
All weapons whatsoever, wrought by man.
You must go for him with your hands, your bare hands.'

Thus spake King Hrothgar and from his bounteous heart
Wished the youth well ...

                    There was loud revelry of heroes,
Bold merriment of men, and minstrel song
And the soothing voice of the harp – until twilight,
The drowsy hour of Grendel's coming, the black shape
Stealing over the dusky moor. Then the Danes
Man by man uprose and, clearing the banquet,
Brought for their guests soft couches, pillow-strewn,
With fleeces of thick wool ...

Straightway Beowulf stripped off his armour, his mailcoat,

His shining helmet. His shield and precious sword
Gave he to his servant, and in the ring of warriors
Lay down to rest. But spent as they were –
For tumult of Grendel and his havoc, like runaway hooves
Making riot in their brains – they could not sleep.
Under their fleeces in terror they sweated and trembled,
Wide-awake, till at last, outworn with weariness,
Heavy-lidded, they slept – all but Beowulf.
Alone, he watched.

                          Over the misty moor
From the dark and dripping caves of his grim lair,
Grendel with fierce ravenous stride came stepping.
A shadow under the pale moon he moved,
That fiend from hell, foul enemy of God,
Toward Heorot. He beheld it from afar, the gleaming roof
Towering high to heaven. His tremendous hands
Struck the studded door, wrenched it from the hinges
Till the wood splintered and the bolts burst apart.
Angrily he prowled over the polished floor,
A terrible light in his eyes – a torch flaming!
As he scanned the warriors, deep-drugged in sleep,
Loud loud he laughed, and pouncing on the nearest
Tore him limb from limb and swallowed him whole,
Sucking the blood in streams, crunching the bones.
Half-gorged, his gross appetite still unslaked,
Greedily he reached his hand for the next – little reckoning
For Beowulf. The youth clutched it and firmly grappled.
Such torture as this the fiend had never known.
In mortal fear, he was minded to flee to his lair,

But Beowulf prisoned him fast. Spilling the benches,
They tugged and heaved, from wall to wall they hurtled.
And the roof rang to their shouting, the huge hall
Rocked, the strong foundations groaned and trembled ...
                                        Alone, Beowulf
Tore Grendel's arm from his shoulder asunder,
Wrenched it from the root while the tough sinews cracked.
And the monster roared in anguish, well knowing
That deadly was the wound and his mortal days ended.
Wildly lamenting, away into the darkness he limped,
Over the misty moor to his gloomy home.
But the hero rejoiced in his triumph and wildly waved
In the air his blood-soaked trophy.

                        And the sun,
God's beacon of brightness, banishing night,
Made glad the sky of morning. From near and far
The Danes came flocking to Heorot to behold
The grisly trophy – Grendel's giant arm
Nailed to the wall, the fingertips outspread,
With nails of sharpened steel and murderous spikes
Clawing the roof. Having drunk their fill of wonder,
Eagerly they followed his track to the lake, and there
Spellbound they stared at the water welling with blood,
Still smoking hot where down to the joyless deep
He had dived, downward to death. And they praised Beowulf
And swore that of all men under the sun, beyond measure
Mightiest was he and fittest to govern his people.

Notes on The Princess in the Suit of Leather

In this Egyptian tale the king loses his wife and is grief stricken. Unable to imagine how any woman could ever replace her, he takes up the suggestion of one of his servants: why not marry his daughter, or else he could one day lose her as well ...

What do you think?
The king's decision is bound to strike us as foolish and wrong. But many of the stories in this collection deal with behaviour that seems exaggerated or unreal. Once we get beyond our reaction of 'but that just wouldn't happen!', we can begin to think about what the story might be telling us.

What is there in the king's situation at the start of the story that might just make him agree to the old woman's plan?

Questions
1. Why do you think the old woman suggests the king marry his daughter?
2. Why does no-one object to the plan?
3. Think about the way the girl responds to her dilemma. What qualities does she have that enable her to find happiness in the end?
4. The story of what happens to her at the sultan's palace seems to form a rag-to-riches story in its own right. What would the story lose if it didn't end with the marriage of the prince and princess?
5. The princess is clearly a heroine, but how do you see her father – villain or victim?

The Princess in the Suit of Leather

Neither here nor elsewhere lived a king who had a wife
whom he loved with all his heart and a daughter who was
the light of his eyes. The princess had hardly reached
womanhood when the queen fell ill and died. For one
whole year the king kept vigil, sitting with bowed head
beside her tomb. Then he summoned the matchmakers,
elderly women wise in the ways of living, and said, 'I
wish to marry again. Here is my poor queen's anklet. Find
me the girl, rich or poor, humble or well-born, whose foot
this anklet will fit. For I promised the queen as she lay
dying that I would marry that girl and no other.'

The matchmakers traveled up and down the kingdom
looking for the king's new bride. But search and search as
they would, they could not find a single girl around
whose ankle the jewel would close. The queen had been
such that there was no woman like her. Then one old
woman said, 'We have entered the house of every maiden
in the land except the house of the king's own daughter.
Let us go to the palace.'

When they slipped the anklet on to the princess's foot,
it suited as if it had been made to her measure. Out of the
seraglio went the women at a run, straight into the king's
presence, and said, 'We have visited every maiden in your
kingdom, but none was able to squeeze her foot into the
late queen's anklet. None, that is, except the princess your
daughter. She wears it as easily as if it were her own.' A
wrinkled matron spoke up: 'Why not marry the princess?

Why give her to a stranger and deprive yourself?' The words were hardly spoken when the king summoned the *qadi* to pen the papers for the marriage. To the princess he made no mention of his plan.

Now there was a bustle in the palace as the jewelers, the clothiers, and the furnishers came to outfit the bride. The princess was pleased to know that she was to be wed. But who her husband was she had no inkling. As late as the 'night of the entering', when the groom first sees the bride, she remained in ignorance even though the servants with their whispers were busy around her, combing and pinning and making her beautiful. At last the minister's daughter, who had come to admire her in her finery, said, 'Why are you frowning? Were not women created for marriage with men? And is there any man whose standing is higher than the king's?'

'What is the meaning of such talk?' cried the princess. 'I won't tell you,' said the girl, 'unless you give me your golden bangle to keep.' The princess pulled off the bracelet, and the girl explained how everything had come about so that the bridegroom was no other than the princess's own father.

The princess turned whiter than the cloth on her head and trembled like one who is sick with the forty-day fever. She rose to her feet and sent away all who were with her. Then, knowing only that she must escape, she ran on to the terrace and leaped over the palace wall, landing in a tanner's yard which lay below. She pressed a handful of gold into the tanner's palm and said, 'Can you make me a suit of leather to hide me from head to heels, showing nothing but my eyes? I want it by tomorrow's dawn?'

The poor man was overjoyed to earn the coins. He set to work with his wife and children. Cutting and stitching through the night they had the suit ready, before it was light enough to know a white thread from a dark. Wait a little! and here comes our lady, the princess. She put on the suit – such a strange spectacle that anyone looking at her would think he was seeing nothing but a pile of hides. In this disguise she left the tanner and lay down beside the city gate, waiting for the day.

Now to return to my lord the king. When he entered the bridal chamber and found the princess gone, he sent his army into the city to search for her. Time and again a soldier would stumble upon the princess lying at the gate and ask, 'Have you seen the king's daughter?' And she would reply:

My name is Juleidah for my coat of skins,
My eyes are weak, my sight is dim,
My ears are deaf, I cannot hear.
I care for no one far or near.

When it was day and the city gate was unbarred, she shuffled out until she was beyond the walls. Then she turned her face away from her father's city and fled.

Walking and running, one foot lifting her and one foot setting her down, there was a day when, with the setting of the sun, the princess came to another city. Too weary to travel a step farther, she fell to the ground. Now her resting place was in the shadow of the wall of the women's quarters, the harem of the sultan's palace. A slave girl, leaning from the window to toss out the crumbs from the royal table, noticed the heap of skins on the ground and thought nothing of it. But when she saw two bright eyes staring out at her from the middle of the hides, she sprang back in terror and said to the queen, 'My lady, there is something monstrous crouching under our window. I have seen it, and it looks like nothing less than an Afreet!' 'Bring it up for me to see and judge,' said the queen.

The slave girl went down shivering with fear, not knowing which was the easier thing to face, the monster outside or her mistress's rage should she fail to do her bidding. But the princess in her suit made no sound when the slave girl tugged at a corner of the leather. The girl took courage and dragged her all the way into the presence of the sultan's wife.

Never had such an astonishing creature been seen in that country. Lifting both palms in amazement, the queen asked her servant, 'What is it?' and then turned to the monster and asked, 'Who are you?' When the heap of skins answered –

My name is Juleidah for my coat of skins,
My eyes are weak, my sight is dim,
My ears are deaf, I cannot hear.
I care for no one far or near.

– how the queen laughed at the quaint reply! 'Go bring food and drink for our guest,' she said, holding her side. 'We shall keep her to amuse us.' When Juleidah had eaten, the queen said, 'Tell us what you can do, so that we may put you to work about the palace.' 'Anything you ask me to do, I am ready to try,' said Juleidah. Then the queen called, 'Mistress cook! Take this broken-winged soul into your kitchen. Maybe for her sake God will reward us with His blessings.'

So now our fine princess was a kitchen skivvy, feeding the fires and raking out the ashes. And whenever the queen lacked company and felt bored, she called Juleidah and laughed at her prattle.

One day the *wazir* sent word that all the sultan's harem was invited to a night's entertainment in his house. All day long there was a stir of excitement in the women's quarters. As the queen prepared to set out in the evening, she stopped by Juleidah and said, 'Won't you come with us tonight? All the servants and slaves are invited. Aren't you afraid to stay alone?' But Juleidah only repeated her refrain:

My ears are deaf, I cannot hear.
I care for no one far or near.

One of the serving girls sniffed and said, 'What is there to make her afraid? She is blind and deaf and wouldn't notice an Afreet even if he were to jump on top of her in the dark!' So they left.

In the women's reception hall of the *wazir's* house there was dining and feasting and music and much merriment. Suddenly, at the height of the talk and enjoyment, such a one entered that they all stopped in the middle of the word they were speaking. Tall as a cypress, with a face like a rose and the silks and jewels of a king's bride, she seemed to fill the room with light. Who was it? Juleidah, who had shaken off her coat of leather as soon as the sultan's harem had gone. She had followed them to the *wazir's*, and now the ladies who had been so merry began to quarrel, each wanting to sit beside the newcomer.

When dawn was near, Juleidah took a handful of gold sequins from the fold of her sash and scattered them on the floor. The ladies scrambled to pick up the bright treasure. And while they were occupied, Juleidah left the hall. Quickly, quickly she raced back to the palace kitchen and put on the coat of leather. Soon the others returned. Seeing the heap of hides on the kitchen floor, the queen poked it with the toe of her red slipper and said, 'Truly, I wish you had been with us to admire the lady who was at the entertainment.' But Juleidah only mumbled, 'My eyes are weak, I cannot see ...' and they all went to their own beds to sleep.

When the queen woke up next day, the sun was high in the sky. As was his habit, the sultan's son came in to kiss his mother's hand and bid her good morning. But she could talk only of the visitor at the *wazir's* feast. 'O my son,' she sighed, 'it was a woman with such a face and such a neck and such a form that all who saw her said, 'She is the daughter of neither a king nor a sultan, but of someone greater yet!' On and on the queen poured out her praises of the woman, until the prince's heart was on fire. Finally his mother concluded, 'I wish I had asked her father's name so that I could engage her to be your bride.' And the sultan's son replied, 'When you return tonight to continue your entertainment, I shall stand outside the *wazir's* door and wait until she leaves. I'll ask her then about her father and her station.'

At sunset the women dressed themselves once more. With the folds of their robes smelling of orange blossom and incense and their bracelets chinking on their arms, they passed by Juleidah lying on the kitchen floor and said, 'Will you come with us tonight?' But Juleidah only turned her back on them. Then as soon as they were safely gone, she threw off her suit of leather and hurried after them.

In the *wazir's* hall the guests pressed close around Juleidah, wanting to see her and ask where she came from. But to all their questions she gave no answer, whether yes or no, although she sat with them until the dawning of the day. Then she threw a fistful of pearls on the marble tiles, and while the women pushed one another to catch them, she slipped away as easily as a hair is pulled out of the dough.

Now who was standing at the door? The prince, of course. He had been waiting for this moment. Blocking her path, he grasped her arm and asked who her father was and from what land she came. But the princess had to be back in her kitchen or her secret would be known. So she fought to get away, and in the scuffle, she pulled the prince's ring clean off his hand. 'At least tell me where you come from!' he shouted after her as she ran. 'By Allah, tell me where!' And she replied, 'I live in a land of paddles and ladles.' Then she fled into the palace and hid in her coat of hides.

In came the others, talking and laughing. The prince told his mother what had taken place and announced that he intended to make a journey. 'I must go to the land of the paddles and ladles,' he said. 'Be patient, my son,' said the queen. 'Give me time to prepare your provisions.' Eager as he was, the prince agreed to delay his departure for two days – 'But not one hour more!'

Now the kitchen became the busiest corner of the palace. The grinding and sieving, the kneading and. the baking began and Juleidah stood watching. 'Away with you,' cried the cook, 'this is no work for you!' 'I want to serve the prince our master like the rest!' said Juleidah. Willing and not willing to let her help, the cook gave her a piece of dough to shape. Juleidah began to make a cake, and when no one was watching, she pushed the prince's ring inside it. And when the food was packed Juleidah placed her own little cake on top of the rest.

Early on the third morning the rations were strapped

into the saddlebags, and the prince set off with his servants and his men. He rode without slackening until the sun grew hot. Then he said, 'Let us rest the horses while we ourselves eat a mouthful.' A servant, seeing Juleidah's tiny loaf lying on top of all the rest, flung it to one side. 'Why did you throw that one away?' asked the prince. 'It was the work of the creature Juleidah; I saw her make it,' said the servant. 'It is as misshapen as she is.' The prince felt pity for the strange half-wit and asked the servant to bring back her cake. When he tore open the loaf, look, his own ring was inside! The ring he lost the night of the *wazir's* entertainment. Understanding now where lay the land of ladles and paddles, the prince gave orders to turn back.

When the king and queen had greeted him, the prince said, 'Mother, send me my supper with Juleidah.' 'She can barely see or even hear,' said the queen. 'How can she bring your supper to you?' 'I shall not eat unless Juleidah brings the food,' said the prince. So when the time came, the cooks arranged the dishes on a tray and helped Juleidah lift it on to her head. Up the stairs she went, but before she reached the prince's room she tipped the dishes and sent them crashing to the floor. 'I told you she cannot see,' the queen said to her son. 'And I will only eat what Juleidah brings,' said the prince.

The cooks prepared a second meal, and when they had balanced the loaded tray upon Juleidah's head, they sent two slave girls to hold her by either hand and guide her to the prince's door. 'Go,' said the prince to the two slaves, 'and you, Juleidah, come.' Juleidah began to say,

My eyes are weak, my sight is dim
I'm called Juleidah for my coat of skins,
My ears are deaf, I cannot hear,
I care for no one far or near.

But the prince told her, 'Come and fill my cup.' As she approached, he drew the dagger that hung at his side and slashed her leather coat from collar to hem. It fell into a heap upon the floor – and there stood the maiden his mother had described, one who could say to the moon, 'Set that I may shine in your stead.'

Hiding Juleidah in a corner of the room, the prince sent for the queen. Our mistress cried out when she saw the pile of skins upon the floor. 'Why, my son, did you bring her death upon your neck? The poor thing deserved your pity more than your punishment!' 'Come in, Mother,' said the prince. 'Come and look at our Juleidah before you mourn her.' And he led his mother to where our fine princess sat revealed, her fairness filling the room like a ray of light. The queen threw herself upon the girl and kissed her on this side and on that, and bade her sit with the prince and eat. Then she summoned the *qadi* to write the paper that would bind our lord the prince to the fair princess, after which they lived together in the sweetest bliss.

Now we make our way back to the king, Juleidah's

father. When he entered the bridal chamber to unveil his own daughter's face and found her gone, and when he had searched the city in vain for her, he called his minister and his servants and dressed himself for travel. From country to country he journeyed, entering one city and leaving the next, taking with him in chains the old woman who had first suggested to him that he marry his own daughter. At last he reached the city where Juleidah was living with her husband the prince.

Now, the princess was sitting in her window when they entered the gate, and she knew them as soon as she saw them. Straightway she sent to her husband urging him to invite the strangers. Our lord went to meet them and succeeded in detaining them only after much pressing, for they were impatient to continue their quest. They dined in the prince's guest hall, then thanked their host and took leave with the words, 'The proverb says: 'Have your fill to eat, but then up, on to your feet!'' – while he delayed them further with the proverb, 'Where you break your bread, there spread out your bed!'

In the end the prince's kindness forced the tired strangers to lie in his house as guests for the night. 'But why did you single out these strangers?' the prince asked Juleidah. 'Lend me your robes and headcloth and let me go to them,' she said. 'Soon you will know my reasons.'

Thus disguised, Juleidah sat with her guests. When the coffee cups had been filled and emptied, she said, 'Let us tell stories to pass the time. Will you speak first, or shall I?' 'Leave us to our sorrows, my son,' said the king her father. 'We have not the spirit to tell tales.' 'I'll entertain you, then, and distract your mind,' said Juleidah. 'There once was a king,' she began, and went on to tell the history of her own adventures from the beginning to the end. Every now and then the old woman would interrupt and say, 'Can you find no better story than this, my son?' But Juleidah kept right on, and when she had finished she said, 'I am your daughter the princess, upon whom all these troubles fell through the words of this old sinner and daughter of shame!'

In the morning they flung the old woman over a tall cliff into the *wadi*. Then the king gave half his kingdom to his daughter and the prince, and they lived in happiness and contentment until death, the parter of the truest lovers, divided them.

Notes on The Invisible One

The story you are about to read exists in almost every country and in hundreds of different versions. We found this particular one on the website of a Canadian Indian group, the Mi'kmaq Nation, but you could find similar versions in ninth-century China; fifteenth-century Italy; seventeenth-century France and nineteenth-century Germany.

Here's how the story reached the website:

It crossed the Atlantic with French fur traders who settled in Canada and had good relationships with the local native people. About 1870, a Mi'kmaq storyteller reworked the tale and told it to a Christian missionary, who added it to his collection of Mi'kmaq stories. In 1884, another writer put it in his book of general Indian groups across Canada and America. In 1992 it appeared as an illustrated children's storybook by Rafe Martin, The Burnt Face Girl. In 1996 a current member of the Mi'kmaq in Nova Scotia put the story and its history on their website.

What do you think?
As you read the story see if it reminds you of a British fairystory, or perhaps a pantomime. If you don't spot the resemblance straight away, try thinking about:
- the test a girl must pass before she is allowed to marry the mighty hunter
- how the members of the old man's family treat the youngest daughter
- the difference between how the girl looks and what she achieves
- who succeeds and who loses out.

Questions
1. What kind of a story do you expect as soon as you read the opening sentence?
2. In what ways does the story meet your expectations?
3. None of the characters have proper names. How does this affect your reaction to the story?
4. Which words make you think this is an old story?
5. Which words or phrases suggest the story has been spoken aloud to the person who wrote it down?

The Invisible One

There was once a large Indian village situated on the border of a lake. At the end of this place was a lodge, in which dwelt a being who was always invisible – a mighty hunter, whose sign was the moose, Stupendous Deity of the spirit world. He had a sister who attended to all his wants, and it was known that any girl who could see him might marry him. There were indeed few who did not make the trial, but it was long ere one succeeded.

And it passed in this wise. Towards evening, when the Invisible One was supposed to be returning home, his sister would walk with any girls who came down to the shore of the lake. She indeed could see her brother, since to her he was always visible, and beholding him, she would say to her companions, 'Do you see my brother?'

They would mostly answer 'Yes,' though some said 'Nay.'

Then the sister would say 'Of what is his shoulder strap made?' Or, as some tell the tell, she would inquire other things such as 'What makes the harness of his sled?'

They would reply 'a strip of rawhide', or 'a length of rope', or something of that kind. Then she, knowing they had not told the truth, would reply quietly 'Very well, let us return to the wigwam.'

When they entered the place, she would bid them not to take a certain seat, for it was his. After they had helped to cook the supper, they would wait with great curiosity to see him eat. Truly he gave proof that he was a real person, for as he took off his moccasins they became visible, and his sister hung them up; but beyond that they beheld nothing, not even when they remained all night as many did.

There dwelt in the village an old man, a widower with three daughters. The youngest of these was very small, weak and often ill, which did not prevent her sisters, especially the eldest, treating her with great cruelty. The second daughter was kinder and sometimes took the part of the poor abused little girl, but the other would burn her hands and face with hot coals. Yes, her whole body was scarred with the marks made by torture, so that people called her Burnt-Skin Girl.

When her father, coming home, asked what it meant that the child was so disfigured, her sister would promptly say that it was the fault of the girl herself, for that having been forbidden to go near the fire, she had disobeyed and fallen in.

Now it came to pass that it entered the heads of the two older sisters of this poor girl that they would go and try their fortune at seeing the Invisible One. So they clad themselves in their finest and strove to look their fairest; and finding his sister at home went with her to take the wonted walk down to the water. Then when He came, being asked if they saw him, they said 'Certainly', and also replied to the question about the shoulder strap saying 'a piece of rawhide.' In saying which they lied, like the rest, for they had seen nothing and got nothing for their pains.

When their father came home the next evening he brought with him many of the little shells from which wampum was made, and they were soon busy stringing the shell beads.

That day, poor little Burnt-Face Girl, who had always run barefoot, got a pair of her father's old moccasins and put them into water that they might become flexible to wear. And begging her sisters for a few wampum shells, the eldest did but call her a 'lying little pest', but the other gave her a few.

Having no clothes beyond a few paltry rags, the poor creature went forth and got herself from the woods a few sheets of birch bark. She made herself a dress of this, putting some figures on the bark by scraping it. This dress she shaped like those worn of old. So she made a petticoat and a loose gown, a cap, leggings and handkerchief, and, having put on her father's great old moccasins – which came nearly up to her knees – she went forth to try her luck.

For even this little thing wished to see the Invisible One in the great wigwam at the end of the village.

Truly her luck had a most inauspicious beginning, for there was one long storm of ridicule and hisses, yells and hoots, from her own door to that which she went to seek. Her sisters tried to shame her, and bade her stay at home, but she would not obey; and all the idlers, seeing this strange little creature in her odd array, cried 'Shame!' But she went on, for she was greatly resolved; it may be that some spirit had inspired her.

Now this poor small wretch in her mad attire, with her hair singed off and her little face as full of burns and scars as there are holes in a sieve, was, for all this, most kindly received by the sister of the Invisible One, for this noble girl knew more than the outside of things as the world knows them.

As the brown of the evening sky became black, she took her down to the lake. And erelong the girls knew that He had come. Then the sister said 'Do you see him?'

The other replied with awe, 'Truly I do – and He is wonderful!'

'And what is his sled string?'

'It is,' she replied, 'the Rainbow.' And great fear was on her.

'But my sister,' said the other, 'what is his bow-string?'

'His bow-string is the light of the Milky Way.'

'Thou hast seen him,' said the sister. And taking the girl home, she bathed her, and as she washed, all the scars disappeared from her face and body. Her hair grew again, it was very long and like a blackbird's wing. Her eyes were like stars. In all the world there was no such beauty. Then from her treasure she gave her a wedding garment, and adorned her. Under the comb, as she combed her, her hair grew. It was a great marvel to behold.

Then, having done this, she bade her take the wife's seat in the wigwam – that by which her brother sat, the seat next to the door. When He entered, terrible and beautiful, he smiled and said – 'So, we are found out.'

'Yes,' was her reply. So she became his wife.

46

Notes on What are Friends For?

This story from India is based on a situation that would have been familiar to the storyteller's local audience: many people in country areas had to travel a long way from home to find work. The return of the farmer with his hard-earned money would be a cause for celebration back in the village.

What do you think?

The story is a simple and light-hearted one and, like many stories, it depends for its effect on our siding with one character rather than another. Think about how it helps us to do this through making use of contrasts. The storyteller sets up the first pair of contrasts in the opening lines (village versus town). Can you spot the others?

Questions

1. Re-read the opening. Which words used to describe the farmer make sure we are on his side from the beginning?

2. Now look at the way the money-lender is described. How has the writer used adjectives and adverbs to suggest how we might react to him – e.g. 'He gazed *lovingly* at the coins.'

3. Think about the ending. This story is over when our preferred character, the farmer, gets away with his savings intact. But for the money-lender, another story is just beginning – and probably a more serious one. Can you think of any other stories, from books, films or television, which rely on a *series* of events rather than a clear ending? Which kinds of stories to you prefer?

What are Friends For?

A poor farmer had been away from home for many months. There was no work in his village, so he had been forced to leave his family to find work in town. He had worked hard and saved and now he was returning home with his savings tucked into his dhoti.

The sun was a blazing ball of fire overhead and the farmer was exhausted. 'A few minutes rest will give me strength to finish my journey,' he said to himself; and he sank down against the trunk of a shady fig tree. He stretched out his weary legs, closed his eyes and was soon fast asleep.

Grr ... grr ... grrr! a strange, low growling woke him up.

'What's that? What's that?' he mumbled half asleep, turning his head from side to side.

Grr ... grr ... grrr-oaw! The queer, rasping cough grew louder. The farmer could hear the crackling of branches as something moved heavily above him. He opened his eyes wide and looked up. There was a large, brown bear climbing down the tree towards him!

'Ahhhh!' the farmer groaned, shutting his eyes tight and holding his breath. Frozen stiff with fright, he searched wildly in his mind for a way to escape. 'If I get up and run, the bear will chase me and catch me. If I stay where I am, the bear will leap on top of me. Let me be brave. I am a man! I will stand and fight the bear!' And he pulled himself up slowly, his back still against the tree.

The poor, trembling farmer looked up again. The bear was very close to him. It hugged the trunk with both arms as it came down the tree. When it reached the bottom, the farmer moved to the opposite side of the tree and grabbed hold of the bear's paws. The tree trunk was between them as they faced each other. The farmer held one of the bear's paws tight in each hand and they circled slowly round and round the tree as if they were dancing. As they moved the coins that had been carefully tucked away in the farmer's dhoti fell tinkling to the ground, one at a time.

At that moment a rich money-lender was passing by. As soon as he heard the tinkling of the coins he stopped. He traced the sweet sound of money to the shady fig tree and when he looked closely, he couldn't believe his eyes. The farmer and the bear, solemnly facing each other, were moving round and round the tree in graceful harmony, one step at a time. And they were holding hands! The money-lender's jaw fell open in astonishment.

'A man and a bear dancing round a tree together!' he exclaimed. 'And on the ground a heap of glittering coins which no one has bothered to pick up?'

The money-lender gazed lovingly at the coins. Then he approached the farmer. 'Dear friend,' he said, his voice as smooth and as sweet as honey. 'I've never seen such a strange sight. Please tell me what's happening.'

The poor farmer was circling the tree thinking sadly 'Will I ever see my family again?'

When he heard the money-lender's oily voice, he replied quickly 'Ah, my good friend. You say it's a strange sight? Wait till I tell you the whole story. You won't believe it!'

The money-lender moved closer, licking his lips.

'The coins you see on the ground come from the bear,' said the farmer.

'From the bear?' echoed the money-lender.

'Yes!' said the farmer. 'From the bear. Each time we go around the tree, money drops from the bear's backside. The more times we go around, the more money comes out … It's simple!'

The money-lender's eyes lit up with greed as he thought 'Here's an easy way to make money. It won't be difficult to trick this stupid fellow.' Then, tapping the farmer gently on his shoulder, his voice full of tenderness, he whispered 'You look tired, my good friend, going round and round and round. Let me help you. I'll take your place while you have a rest. After all, what are friends for?'

Wearily, the poor farmer nodded and the money-lender eagerly took his place grabbing the bear's paws firmly in his own hands. Immediately, they started to move round the tree trunk in circles – the rich money-lender and the bear.

Heaving a great sigh of relief, the poor farmer gathered up all his coins from the ground. He tied them firmly into his dhoti once again and set off home. Just before he turned on to the main path, he looked back. The rich money-lender was *still* smiling sweetly, holding the bear's paws firmly in his hands, the tree between them, going round and round and round ...

What Does a Story Mean?

Notes on The Wicked King and his Good Son

This story from Indian mythology appears here in a modern version retold by Madhur Jaffrey in her collection *Seasons of Splendour*, where she has arranged the stories as they might be told at festivals over the course of a year. The Hindi word for spring is 'Holi' – which also forms part of the name of the king's sister, Holika, in the story. In her introduction, Madjur Jaffrey tells how her family always built a huge bonfire at the spring festival and how they referred to this as 'burning Holi'.

What do you think?

At the start of the story, King Hiranya Kashyap is described as good looking, rich and powerful. 'What more could anyone want?' asks the storyteller – and, of course, we instantly suspect that he will not be satisfied with his lot.

Do you know any other stories where a character who seems to have everything goes one step too far?

As you read the story of the king's downfall, consider the parts played by:

- the wise sage
- the king's own character.

Questions

1. Why does everything change for Hiranya and Holika when Prahlad is born?
2. How does Prahlad come to challenge his father's powers?
3. Look at the ending of the story. Can you think of any reasons why this story might be especially appropriate for the festival of spring?

The Wicked King and his Good Son

Hiranya Kashyap thought very highly of himself. He was good looking, rich – and he was the King. What more could anyone want? One day, a wise Sage, who could see into the past and the future, came to him and said, 'Your majesty, according to what I see in the stars, you cannot be killed by man, beast or weapons, during the day or during the night, on earth or in water, inside a house or, indeed, outside it.'

That, as far as King Hiranya Kashyap was concerned, made him immortal. If he was arrogant before, he now became unbearable and was very cruel to those subjects who did not flatter him endlessly. If he said, 'This bread is stale,' all his palace cooks would have to agree and throw it out, even if they had just cooked it. If he said, 'The River Ganges flows up from the sea to the Himalaya Mountains,' all the courtiers would have to nod their heads in agreement even though they knew that the Ganges began as a series of cool, icy trickles from the cracks of the world's highest mountains and then flowed, slowly and gracefully, down to the sea.

The sad fact of the matter was that Hiranya Kashyap thought he was God. Not only did he make his subjects kneel and pray to him but he bullied and tortured those who did not.

He had a sister called Holika who had been told by the same wise Sage that she could never be burnt by fire. Hiranya Kashyap and Holika became so vain that they behaved as if they were owners of the entire universe.

Then, one day, all this changed.

Hiranya Kashyap's wife gave birth to a baby boy whom they named Prahlad.

Hiranya Kashyap found no need, or time, to rejoice.

When the courtiers came to him and said, 'Congratulations, your majesty, on the birth of your heir,' he only snarled, saying, 'Bah, what do I need an heir for? I shall live forever. I am God. Heirs mean nothing to me.'

One day, when Prahlad was four, he was playing outside the potter's kiln and saw the potter praying.

'What are you doing?' he asked.

'I am praying to God to save my kittens,' she replied. 'They have got locked up in the kiln by accident.'

'You should pray to my father,' said Prahlad.

'Your father cannot save my kittens from that awful fire inside,' she said, 'only God can.'

'My father will punish you if you use God's name,' Prahlad advised her.

'I'll have to take my chances,' the potter replied.

'Your God can do nothing to help,' Prahlad said.

'Oh yes he can,' the potter answered.

'Then I'll wait here and see,' the young boy said. Prahlad waited. When it was time to open the kiln, he heard, 'Meaow, meaow.' It was the kittens. They were safe!

A year later, when Prahlad was five and was playing in the garden, his father chanced to pass that way. The King paused long enough to ask his son, 'Who is the greatest being in the whole Universe?' He expected the same answer he got from all his flatterers.

'God,' said the child.

The King was taken aback for a second. Then he smirked. 'See, see,' he boasted to his courtiers, 'even this small child recognizes that I am God.'

'No,' said the child, 'you are not God. You are the King and that is all you will ever be.'

Hiranya Kashyap's face turned purple with rage. 'Take this child,' he ordered, 'and hurl him from the highest cliff in the kingdom.'

The courtiers were very fond of the gentle child but were terrified of his father. So they scooped little Prahlad up and carried him to the highest mountain in the Himalayas. There, they stood on a peak that touched the sky and dropped the boy.

Prahlad fell ... fell ... fell. But to his surprise – and to that of the courtiers looking down from above – he landed in the midst of the warmest, sweetest softness that could be imagined. God had been watching from his heavenly window and had decided to catch the child in his lap.

When Hiranya Kashyap found out what had happened, he turned black with anger. He had the boy brought to the court and thrown at his feet.

'You were very lucky to be saved,' he raged.

'It was God who saved me,' Prahlad replied.

'As I was saying,' the King continued angrily, 'you were lucky to land in such a soft patch. The courtiers who threw you down there will have their heads chopped off and then I'm going to have a roaring fire made and have you burnt in it. Let us see what your God can do for you then!'

The King commanded that a huge bonfire be made the following day. Logs were collected and piled into a massive pyre. Then the pyre was lit.

Hiranya Kashyap called his sister, Holika, and said, 'If we just toss this child into the fire, he will squirm and run out. Since you have been granted the boon of never being burnt by fire, why don't you take Prahlad in your arms, walk into the flames and sit down. Hold the child tightly. When he is quite dead, you can walk out.'

Holika took Prahlad in her arms and walked into the middle of the fire. There, she put him in her lap and sat down.

The flames were leaping hundreds of feet into the sky. Hiranya Kashyap was quite pleased with himself. He was finally getting rid of this troublesome child.

The flames were very hot and made the King perspire. At first he contented himself with moving back a few yards. Then, when the heat and smoke became quite overwhelming, he said to his courtiers, 'I'm going into my cool palace. Let me know when all this is over.'

A strange thing happened amidst the flames. Holika had a change of heart. She looked up towards heaven and prayed, 'God, please do not save me from the fire. I am ready to meet my Maker. But please save this innocent life. I give my boon to this young boy. Let him live.'

The fire burnt for several hours. The King had just sat down to enjoy his dinner when one of his courtiers came running in.

'Your majesty,' he said bowing, 'your majesty.'

'Yes, yes, what is it? You know I do not like being disturbed at dinner time.'

'The fire has burnt itself out.'

'And?' prompted the King.

'Holika has perished in the flames.'

'What!' cried the King, 'And the child?'

'Your majesty … Well, your majesty …'

'Well, what? Answer quickly or I'll have your tongue pulled out.'

'Prahlad is still alive.'

Hiranya Kashyap kicked his food away and stood on his feet, puffed up with fury like a balloon.

'Bring that brat to me. I'll kill him myself.'

The courtiers dragged in little Prahlad and threw him in front of his father.

'So,' said the father, 'you managed to escape a second time.'

'I did not escape,' said Prahlad, 'God saved me.'

'God, God,' cried the King, 'I'm sick of your God. Where is he anyway?'

'He is everywhere – in fire, water – even in that pillar.'

'Oh, he is in that pillar, is he?' the King yelled. 'Well, I am going to tie you up to that same pillar and kill you. Let's see if your God will come out to save you.'

Prahlad was tied up to the pillar and Hiranya Kashyap raised his sword to finish him off. Just then, there was a loud thunderclap and the pillar broke in two.

Out of the pillar came God.

He had assumed a strange shape.

The upper part of the body was that of a lion, the lower that of a man.

So he was neither man nor beast.

He lifted the King and carried him to the threshold of the palace and then placed him in his lap.

So the King was neither in a house nor outside it.

Then he killed Hiranya Kashyap with one swipe of his long lion's claws.

So no weapon was used.

The time of the day was dusk.

So it was neither morning nor night.

Pink and grey clouds puffed along in the sky. Hiranya Kashyap was finally dead, despite all his arrogant predictions.

The courtiers cried, 'Long live the King,' as they placed the young Prahlad on his father's throne, happy in the knowledge that they were now going to be ruled with justice.

Notes on Whose Footprints?

The character of Legba, the mischievous servant, has many counterparts in stories from all over the world. You could meet him as Hermes, Anansi, Coyote, Puck – all trickster figures who are said to 'threaten boundaries'. They are always irrepressible characters, a bit like Bugs Bunny, obeying their own instincts rather than following the rules.

What do you think?
- In what ways does God in this story act as you would expect?
- Do you find any of his behaviour 'un-godlike'?

Questions
1. What is the general opinion of Legba among the people at the start of the story?
2. Why does God choose not to defend his servant to the people?
3. What explanation does the story offer us for why God stopped living among his people on earth?
4. Look again at the beginning and end of the story. Do you think the people of Abomey were better off when God lived among them or when he moved up into the sky?

Whose Footprints?

Do you suppose God made the world all by himself? Of course not. He had help. He had a servant. Every Fon in Abomey knows that. The servant's name was Legba, and he took the blame for whatever went wrong.

Whenever the people saw a wonderful sunset, or made a huge catch of fish, they gave thanks to God and said, 'Great is our Creator, who has made all things wonderfully well!'

Whenever they fell over a rock, or the canoe sank, they said, 'Legba is making mischief again. That villain Legba!'

Now Legba thought this was mortally unfair. 'Why do I get all the blame?' he complained.

'That's what you're there for,' said God. 'It wouldn't do for people to think of God as anything but perfect. It would set them a bad example.'

'But they hate me!' protested Legba. 'They hang up charms at their doors to keep me out, and they frighten their children with my name: 'Be good or Legba will come and steal you out of your bed!' How would you feel?' But God had already sauntered away towards the garden where he grew yams. (This was in the days when God lived on Earth, among all that he had made.)

God tended those yams with loving care and attention. If the truth were told, he was kept so busy by his gardening some days, that things could go wrong in the world without him really noticing. It did not matter. Legba got the blame, naturally.

Legba sat down and thought. Then Legba stood up and spoke. 'Lord, I hear that thieves are planning to steal your yams tonight!'

God was horrified. He sounded a ram's-horn trumpet and summoned together all the people of the world. They came, jostling and bowing, smiling and offering presents. They were rather taken aback to see God so angry.

'If any one of you intends to rob my garden tonight, I'm telling you here and I'm telling you now, and I'm making it plain as day: that thief shall die!'

The people clutched each other and trembled. They nodded feverishly to show they had understood, hurried home to their beds and pulled the covers over their heads until morning. God watched them scatter and brushed together the palms of his great hands. 'That settles that,' he said, and went home to bed himself.

Legba waited. When all sound had ceased but the scuttle of night creatures, the flutter of bats and the drone of snoring humanity, he crept into God's house. God, too, was snoring. Legba wormed his way across the floor, and stole the sandals from beside God's bed.

Putting on the sandals, he crept to the yam garden. Though the shoes were over-large and tripped him more than once, he worked his way from tree to tree, removing every delectable yam. The dew glistened, the ground was wet. The sandals of God left deep prints in the moist soil

'Come quick! Come quick! The thief has struck!'

God tumbled out of bed, fumbled his feet into his sandals and stumbled out of doors into the first light of morning. When he saw the waste that had been laid to his garden, the shout could be heard all the way to Togo.

'Don't worry! Don't worry!' Legba hurried to console him. 'Look how the thief has left his footprints in the ground! You have only to find the shoes that made those footprints, and you will have caught the culprit red-handed … -footed, I mean.'

Once more, the ram's-horn sounded, and the people pelted out of their huts and horded into God's presence, trembling.

'*Someone* has stolen my yams!' bellowed God. '*Someone* is about to *DIE*!'

They all had to fetch out their sandals, and every sandal was laid against the footprints in the garden. But not one fitted. Not one.

'Legba! Try Legba! He's always doing wicked things!' shouted the people, and Legba felt that familiar pang of resentment that God did not correct them. It would have been nice if God could have said, 'Oh not *Legba*! He's entirely trustworthy. He helped me create the world. He's my good and faithful servant.' Not a bit of it.

'*Legba! Have you been stealing from me?!*'

Willingly Legba produced his sandals. Willingly he laid them alongside the footprints in the garden. But not by any stretch of the imagination did Legba's sandals fit the prints beneath the yam trees.

'Perhaps you walked in your sleep, O Lord?' suggested Legba, and the people all said, 'AAAH!'

God tried to look disdainful of such a ridiculous suggestion, but the eyes of all Creation were gazing at him, waiting. He laid his great foot alongside one of the great footprints, and the people gasped and laughed and sighed with relief. It was just God, walking in his sleep, ha ha ha! God was to blame after all!

Then they began to wonder – God could see the question form in their faces – if God had sleepwalked once, perhaps he had sleepwalked before. And if God stole in his sleep, what else might he get up to under the cover of darkness, under the influence of his dreams?

God glowered at Legba. He knew Legba had something to do with his embarrassment, but could not quite see what. Instead, he stamped his sandalled foot irritably and said, 'I'm going! I'm not staying here where no one gives me the respect I deserve! I'm going *higher up*!'

So God moved higher up. And he told Legba to report to him every night, in the sky, with news of what people were getting up to.

Of course what Legba chooses to tell God is entirely up to Legba. But the Fon of Abomey have been a lot nicer to Legba since God went higher up. A lot nicer.

Notes on Deer Hunter and White Corn Maiden

Many cultures tell stories where the characters are linked to particular stars in the night sky. We still refer to some constellations by names from classical mythology – like Castor and Pollux, the twins; or Pegasus, the winged horse. Often, as in this story, when there is no way out of a dilemma, the characters end their life on earth but live on as an outline in the stars.

What do you think?
Most stories put us on the side of the lovers – they are the hero and heroine and so we might expect their love to triumph. Being in love makes these two feel wonderful – but does the power of that love in this story have some destructive effects as well?

Questions
1. Look carefully at the paragraph describing the soul's wanderings during the four days after death. What do you think might lie behind this belief?
2. Why might the villagers be unhappy about Deer Hunter keeping watch beside his wife's body?
3. What is the promise Deer Hunter makes when he tries to persuade his wife's soul to remain with him on earth?
4. How does this promise rebound on him?
5. How would you sum up the message of this story?

Deer Hunter and White Corn Maiden

Long ago in the ancient home of the San Juan people, in a village whose ruins can be seen across the river from present day San Juan, lived two magically gifted young people. The youth was called Deer Hunter because even as a boy, he was the only one who never returned empty-handed from the hunt. The girl, whose name was White Corn Maiden, made the finest pottery, and embroidered clothing with the most beautiful designs, of any woman in the village, and it was no surprise to their parents that they always sought one another's company. Seeing that they were favoured by the gods, the villagers assumed that they were destined to marry.

And in time they did, and contrary to their elders' expectations, they began to spend even more time with one another. White Corn Maiden began to ignore her pottery making and embroidery, while Deer Hunter gave up hunting, at a time when he could have saved many of the people from hunger. They even began to forget their religious obligations. At the request of the pair's worried parents, the tribal elders called a council. This young couple was ignoring all the traditions by which the tribe had lived and prospered, and the people feared that angry gods might bring famine, flood, sickness or some other disaster upon the village, even though it was late spring and all nature had unfolded in new life.

Then suddenly White Corn Maiden became ill, and within three days she died. Deer Hunter's grief had no bounds. He refused to speak or eat, preferring to keep watch beside his wife's body until she was buried early the next day.

For four days after death, every soul wanders in and around its village and seeks forgiveness from those whom it may have wronged in life. It is a time of unease for the living, since the soul may appear in the form of a wind, a disembodied voice, a dream, or even in human shape. To prevent such a visitation, the villagers go to the dead person before burial and utter a soft prayer of forgiveness. And on the fourth day after death, the relatives gather to perform a ceremony releasing the soul into the spirit world, from which it will never return.

But Deer Hunter was unable to accept his wife's death. Knowing that he might see her during the four-day interlude, he began to wander around the edge of the village. Soon he drifted farther out into the fields, and it was here at sundown on the fourth day, even while his relatives were gathering for the ceremony of release, that he potted a small fire near a clump of bushes.

Deer Hunter drew closer and found his wife, as beautiful as she was in life and dressed in all her finery, combing her long hair with a cactus brush in preparation for the last journey. He fell weeping at her feet, imploring her not to leave but to return with him to the village before the releasing rite was consummated. White Corn Maiden begged her husband to let her go, because she no longer belonged to the life of the living. Her return would anger the spirits, she said, and anyhow, soon she would be no longer beautiful, and Deer Hunter would shun her.

He brushed her pleas aside by pledging his undying love and promising that he would let nothing part them. Eventually she relented, saying that she would hold him to his promise. They entered the village just as their relatives were marching to the shrine with the food offering that would release the soul of White Corn Maiden. They were horrified when they saw her, and again they and the village elders begged Deer Hunter to let her go. He ignored them, and an air of grim expectancy settled over the village.

The couple returned to their home, but before many days had passed, Deer Hunter noticed that his wife was beginning to have an unpleasant odor. Then he saw that her beautiful face had grown ashen and her skin dry. At first he only turned his back on her as they slept. Later he began to sit up on the roof all night, but White Corn Maiden always joined him. In time villagers became used to the sight of Deer Hunter racing among the houses and through the fields with White Corn Maiden, now not much more than skin and bones, in hot pursuit.

Things continued on this way, until one misty morning a tall and imposing figure appeared in the small dance court at the center of the village. He was dressed in spotless white buckskin robes and carried the biggest bow anyone had ever seen. On his back was slung a great quiver with the two largest arrows anyone had ever seen.

He remained standing at the centre of the village and called, in a voice that carried into every home, for Deer Hunter and White Corn Maiden. Such was his authority that the couple stepped forward meekly and stood facing him.

The awe-inspiring figure told the couple that he had been sent from the spirit world because they, Deer Hunter and White Corn Maiden, had violated their people's traditions and angered the spirits; that because they had been so selfish, they had brought grief and near-disaster to the village. 'Since you insist on being together,' he said, 'you shall have your wish. You will chase one another across the sky, as visible reminders that your people must live according to tradition if they are to survive.' With this he set Deer Hunter on one arrow and shot him low into the western sky. Putting White Corn Maiden on the other arrow, he placed her just behind her husband.

That evening the villagers saw two new stars in the west. The first, large and very bright, began to move east across the heavens. The second, a smaller, flickering star, followed close behind. So it is to this day, according to the Tewa; the brighter one is Deer hunter, placed there in the prime of his life. The dimmer star is White Corn Maiden, set there after she had died; yet she will forever chase her husband across the heavens.

Notes on John Barleycorn

There are many versions of this story, telling how barley is turned into malt liquor. This one is by the eighteenth-century Scottish poet, Robert Burns – probably best known now for 'Auld Lang Syne' – but it also appears as an English folksong and as a comic tale about American drunks.

What do you think?
The process of turning barley into alcohol seems an unlikely subject for a drama but this was a popular ballad and drinking song. What kind of character does John Barleycorn seem to be?

Questions
1. Each stage of the process of growing the barley and making the drink is turned into a bit of a drama. What is happening to the barley in each season of the year?
2. How would you describe the mood of the story in verses 6 to 11?
3. How does the mood change in the last section of the poem?
4. Do you know any other stories where an important transformation takes place?
5. What particular characteristics of John Barleycorn are celebrated in verses 13 and 14?

John Barleycorn

There were three kings into the east,
   Three kings both great and high;
And they hae sworn a solemn oath
   John Barleycorn should die.

They took a plough and ploughed him down,
   Put clods upon his head;
And they hae sworn a solemn oath
   John Barleycorn was dead.

But the cheerful Spring came kindly on,
   And showers began to fall;
John Barleycorn got up again,
   And sore surprised them all.

The sultry sons of Summer came,
   And he grew thick and strong;
His head weel armed wi' pointed spears,
   That no one should him wrong.

The sober Autumn entered mild,
   When he grew wan and pale;
His bending joints and drooping head
   Showed he began to fail.

His colour sickened more and more,
   He faded into age;
And then his enemies began
   To show their deadly rage.

They've taen a weapon, long and sharp,
   And cut him by the knee;
Then tied him fast upon a cart,
   Like a rogue for forgerie.

They laid him down upon his back,
   And cudgelled him full sore;
They hung him up before the storm,
   And turned him o'er and o'er

They filled up a darksome pit
   With water to the brim;
They heavèd in John Barleycorn,
   There let him sink or swim.

They laid him out upon the floor
   To work him farther wo;
And still, as signs of life appeared,
   They tossed him to and fro.

They wasted o'er a scorching flame
   The marrow of his bones;
But a miller used him worst of all,
   For he crushed him 'tween two stones.

And they hae taen his very heart's blood,
    And drunk it round and round;
And still the more and more they drank,
    Their joy did more abound.

John Barleycorn was a hero bold,
    Of noble enterprise;
For if you do but taste his blood,
    'Twill make your courage rise.

'Twill make a man forget his wo;
    'Twill heighten all his joy:
'Twill make the widow's heart to sing,
    Though the tear were in her eye.

Then let us toast John Barleycorn,
    Each man a glass in hand;
And may his great posterity
    Ne'er fail in old Scotland!

Notes on How Coyote Stole Fire

We can't live without fire, so many countries have their own stories to explain how they first got hold of it. Coyote appears in many American Indian stories, where he is always cunning and resourceful. He is a prairie wolf – we would probably call him a wild dog.

What do you think?
Why is the gift of fire so important to the human beings in this story?

Questions
1. How does the story suggest early human beings were more in touch with their natural surroundings?
2. The storyteller distinguishes between these human and 'the People', Coyote's group. Who do you think the People might be?
3. What qualities does Coyote have that enable him to outwit the Fire Beings?
4. What is Coyote's final gift to the humans?

How Coyote Stole Fire

Long ago, when man was newly come into the world, there were days when he was the happiest creature of all. Those were the days when spring brushed across the willow tails, or when his children ripened with the blueberries in the sun of summer, or when the goldenrod bloomed in the autumn haze.

But always the mists of autumn evenings grew more chill, and the sun's strokes grew shorter. Then man saw winter moving near, and he became fearful and unhappy. He was afraid for his children, and for the grandfathers and grandmothers who carried in their heads the sacred tales of the tribe. Many of these, young and old, would die in the long, ice-bitter months of winter.

Coyote, like the rest of the People, had no need for fire. So he seldom concerned himself with it, until one spring day when he was passing a human village. There the women were singing a song of mourning for the babies and the old ones who had died in the winter. Their voices moaned like the west wind through a buffalo skull, prickling the hairs on Coyote's neck.

'Feel how the sun is now warm on our backs,' one of the men was saying. 'Feel how it warms the earth and makes these stones hot to the touch. If only we could have had a small piece of the sun in our teepees during the winter.'

Coyote, overhearing this, felt sorry for the men and women. He also felt that there was something he could do to help them. He knew of a faraway mountain-top where the three Fire Beings lived. These Beings kept fire to themselves, guarding it carefully for fear that man might somehow acquire it and become as strong as they. Coyote saw that he could do a good turn for man at the expense of these selfish Fire Beings.

So Coyote went to the mountain of the Fire Beings and crept to its top, to watch the way that the Beings guarded their fire. As he came near, the Beings leaped to their feet and gazed searchingly round their camp. Their eyes glinted like bloodstones, and their hands were clawed like the talons of the great black vulture.

'What's that? What's that I hear?' hissed one of the Beings.

'A thief, skulking in the bushes!' screeched another.

The third looked more closely, and saw Coyote. But he had gone to the mountain-top on all-fours, so the Being thought she saw only an ordinary coyote slinking among the trees.

'It is no one, it is nothing!' she cried, and the other two looked where she pointed and also saw only a grey coyote. They sat down again by their fire and paid Coyote no more attention.

So he watched all day and night as the Fire Beings guarded their fire. He saw how they fed it pine cones and dry branches from the sycamore trees. He saw how they stamped furiously on runaway rivulets of flame that sometimes nibbled outwards on edges of dry grass. He saw also how, at night, the Beings took turns to sit by the fire. Two would sleep while one was on guard; and at certain times the Being by the fire would get up and go into their teepee, and another would come out to sit by the fire.

Coyote saw that the Beings were always jealously watchful of their fire except during one part of the day. That was in the earliest morning, when the first winds of dawn arose on the mountains. Then the Being by the fire would hurry, shivering, into the teepee calling, 'Sister, sister, go out and watch the fire.' But the next Being would always be slow to go out for her turn, her head spinning with sleep and the thin dreams of dawn.

Coyote, seeing all this, went down the mountain and spoke to some of his friends among the People. He told them of hairless man, fearing the cold and death of winter. And he told them of the Fire Beings, and the warmth and brightness of the flame. They all agreed that man should have fire, and they all promised to help Coyote's undertaking.

Then Coyote sped again to the mountain-top. Again the Fire Beings leaped up when he came close, and one cried out, 'What's that? A thief, a thief!'

But again the others looked closely, and saw only a grey coyote hunting among the bushes. So they sat down again and paid him no more attention.

Coyote waited through the day, and watched as night fell and two of the Beings went off to the teepee to sleep. He watched as they changed over at certain times all the night long, until at last the dawn winds rose.

Then the Being on guard called, 'Sister, sister, get up and watch the fire.'

And the Being whose turn it was climbed slow and sleepy from her bed, saying, 'Yes, yes, I am coming. Do not shout so.'

But before she could come out of the teepee, Coyote lunged from the bushes, snatched up a glowing portion of fire, and sprang away down the mountainside.

Screaming, the Fire Beings flew after him. Swift as Coyote ran, they caught up with him, and one of them reached out a clutching hand. Her fingers touched only the tip of the tail, but the touch was enough to turn the hairs white, and coyote tail-tips are white still. Coyote shouted, and flung the fire away from him. But the others of the People had gathered at the mountain's foot, in case they were needed. Squirrel saw the fire falling, and caught it, putting it on her back and fleeing away through the treetops. The fire scorched her back so painfully that her tail curled up and back, as squirrels' tails still do today.

The Fire Beings then pursued Squirrel, who threw the fire to Chipmunk. Chattering with fear, Chipmunk stood still as if rooted until the Beings were almost upon her. Then, as she turned to run, one Being clawed at her, tearing down the length of her back and leaving three stripes that are to be seen on chipmunks' backs even today. Chipmunk threw the fire to Frog, and the Beings turned towards him. One of the Beings grasped his tail, but Frog gave a mighty leap and tore himself free, leaving his tail behind in the Being's hand – which is why frogs have had no tails ever since.

As the Beings came after him again, Frog flung the fire on to Wood. And Wood swallowed it.

The Fire Beings gathered round, but they did not know how to get the fire out of Wood. They promised it gifts, sang to it and shouted at it. They twisted it and struck it and tore it with their knives. But Wood did not give up the fire. In the end, defeated, the Beings went back to their mountain-top and left the People alone.

But Coyote knew how, to get fire out of Wood. And he went to the village of men and showed them how. He showed them the trick of rubbing two dry sticks together, and the trick of spinning a sharpened stick in a hole made in another piece of wood. So man was from then on warm and safe through the killing cold of winter.

The Way You Tell Them

Notes on Under Ben Bulben

This story comes from the Fianna, a group of Irish legends about a hero called Finn MacCool. They were written down during the Middle Ages but would have been told orally many centuries before this. The expeditions they describe are often set in magical surroundings and the characters are not gods but belong to a group of heroes with some superhuman characteristics – Finn, for instance, is supposed to have lived to the age of 230!

Skill in hunting and fighting was greatly valued by the people who shared these stories and storytelling itself was taken very seriously. People believed that just by listening to tales of daring and heroism they would become stronger. At key moments in the stories, the listener is drawn into the action, wondering what will happen next. There are many moments like that in this story, but the most dramatic suspense is at the end. Dermot is injured and only MacCool has the power to save him. Will he do it? Three times he faces a choice and each time it's different – you'll have to read the story to find out how.

What do you think?

Arranged marriages were quite common in Ireland at the time these tales were set and there was a good reason for this. To maintain their strength and broaden their influence, tribal leaders always tried to build links with other tribes through marriage. This was an important means of keeping the community safe and stable. Does this information affect your reaction to Gronnia's rejection of Finn MacCool?

Questions

1. How does the opening of the story encourage us to have some sympathy for Finn MacCool?
2. The storyteller uses two vivid similes to describe the confusion Gronnia feels after meeting Dermot. How would you sum up her dilemma?
3. Angus is not very developed as a character but he plays a crucial role at two points in the story. How do his actions affect events?
4. When Dermot offers to help Finn and his men kill the boar of Ben Bulben, we might expect the story to end with a reconciliation between the two men. Why does this fail to happen?

Under Ben Bulben

Finn MacCool was afraid. He was the leader of the Fianna, the warrior poets. As a young man, he had killed his father's murderer, Goll MacMorna, and from then on everyone in Ireland knew that Finn MacCool was the greatest fighter of them all. He had never been afraid before, which made it all the worse, since he was also afraid of the feeling of fear. For Finn MacCool was growing old.

When an active man gains in weight and loses his hair, he senses time creeping up on him. Maybe time is laughing at him, that he cannot do the things he did before. He is slower than he was, weaker than he was, and for a man who was the fastest and the strongest of his time this is a feeling hard to bear.

There are different ways in which men fight back against time. Some shout and bluster, and pretend that nothing's changed. Others bully weaker men, making them speak the lies that are no longer true. And others look for a younger, beautiful woman, who will show that they are young and strong again. To the men themselves, and the men that envy them, the young woman at their side is a sign that they still have their strength, they are not past their best.

The High King of Ireland had a young and beautiful daughter, the princess Gronnia. Finn MacCool asked to marry her, the king agreed, and a marvellous celebration was arranged. Cattle were killed, gallons of wine prepared, and all the Fianna were invited to the feast. The poets practised their finest songs, to sing the praises of brave MacCool and Gronnia the beautiful.

She was not happy. She was a good daughter, and her father was a wise man, but she was young and full of life. She had not planned on marriage to an aging man. But she had no thought of defying her father – until she saw Dermot O'Doon. He was young, and brave, and handsome, like Finn MacCool had been. There was twenty years between them, and Gronnia had no choice.

She knew her father admired Finn MacCool, and that she could make him happy, simply by becoming his wife. She knew that this was what all Ireland would expect. In her head, that was as clear as Shannon water on a summer day. But in her heart was a burning like the sun, a certainty that she loved Dermot, would do anything to live with him. She would brave her father, leave home and break the heart of Finn MacCool. She would suffer the gossips and the curses, the price of broken vows. She would risk it all.

She stood in a dark corner, waiting for Dermot to notice her. As he saw her, she knew he thought that she was beautiful. But as she told him of her love, she also knew that he was a good man. He was one of the Fianna, who followed MacCool, and by his own action he could not betray that trust. There was only one way in which she could make him go with her.

Without waiting for him to speak, she put Dermot under geasa. A geasa is a solemn oath, which no man can break. She had never met him before, but she knew that he would obey, would run away with her, and love her till he died. She also knew that he would protect her, and fight for her, even against the mighty Finn MacCool.

She put a drug in the barrels of drink, and by the time night came the castle echoed to the sound of drunken snores. Dermot and Gronnia tiptoed silently between sleeping bodies which lay sprawled across the floor. She paused by the throne, where her father slumped asleep, but Dermot took her hand and they left. They rode to the banks of the Shannon, where Dermot carried Gronnia across the wild waters, and built the first shelter they would share.

In the morning MacCool was drowsy. His head ached, and his movements were slow. But when he knew that Gronnia was gone, with his own follower Dermot, then he was wide awake. He was back to the old Finn, fast and fierce and ruthless, desperate for revenge. No young warrior was going to take his wife. He called the Clann Navin, the best trackers in the Fianna, and ordered them to find the couple, and bring his Gronnia back. Nobody asked what would happen to Dermot, but it was not difficult to guess.

The Clann came to the Shannon, but by now it was a torrent, and Dermot had been careful to cover his tracks. On their own, the clan would have given up, and gone back home. They were not on their own. MacCool was at their heels, ready to hang any man who wanted to return. The Clann went on.

Days later, they found a woodland hut. They looked through a gap in the wall, and saw Dermot and Gronnia inside. The hut had seven doors, but the Clann were prepared, and none were ready to return to Finn MacCool, with the news that the young lovers had escaped. So they placed a guard, and waited for daylight to come.

Dermot's foster father was called Angus, and from the druids he had learned the magic arts. He heard music in the wind, the song of danger, which took him to where the couple lay. He could make himself invisible, and joined Dermot and Gronnia in the hut. He offered to take them out, but Dermot was a fighting man, who would not take advantage in this way. So Angus took Gronnia out of the hut, and waited to see if Dermot could escape.

Carefully, quietly, he watched through a crack in the door. Near the end of a long night of waiting, one of the guards was yawning. Very slowly, making no noise, Dermot undid the latch. Then, when the guard was standing near the door, he slammed it hard against him, knocking him over. With a spear in each hand, he raced towards the hills, and none of the Clann were fast enough to catch him. Up there, in a cave, Gronnia was waiting. She had known that she might not ever see him again, and they clung to each other in relief. Then they turned to thank Angus.

He waved their thanks aside. 'Do not dwell on the past. If you are to live, you must look to the time to come, and that will be hard. Listen now to the advice I give, for it may save your life.' He looked serious, thinking hard, trying to remember all he had learnt.

'Never go into a cave with only one entrance, nor on to an island, unless there are two channels leading to it. Do not stay to eat your food where you have cooked it, or eat where you have slept. Last, and most of all, do not sleep in the same place twice.'

So Dermot and Gronnia set off, for a life on the run. Like hunted animals, they moved from place to place, changing their pattern and never leaving clues. Dermot was a good hunter and their love grew, as they clung together in the wind and the cold. Gronnia knew she had chosen well, and was proud to bear his children, but as their family grew so it was harder to keep running. One day, surely, Finn MacCool would lose his anger and they would be free to live in peace.

Angus went to MacCool, who could never forgive Dermot for what he had done. But he was even older, weary of the chase, and hate was making him ill. At the end of a long night's drinking, and finer singing than the Fianna had ever heard, Angus persuaded him. Dermot and Gronnia could settle at a farm, and MacCool would leave them alone.

They brought up their children, raised cattle and walked together through the hills. Sometimes they remembered the night they met, and the oath that Gronnia put on Dermot, to make them run away. They talked, and laughed, and argued, and they knew what it had cost them, but neither of them regretted the choice that they had made.

One night they heard the sound of barking.

'They're not ours. Leave them,' Gronnia said.

'I want to see who's there. It may be Finn MacCool.'

'He's promised. Angus said. Come back, Dermot. It's cold.'

But Dermot was up, and in his boots, and going out to look. The dogs were the dogs of Finn MacCool, but they were not hunting him. They were after the wild boar of Ben Bulben, who had killed more than twenty of his men.

'Do you want a hand?'

Finn looked at Dermot, the warrior he had trained. He saw the man who had stolen his bride, but he also saw why she had gone with him. This was a fine, brave, strong young man, just like the young MacCool. But he spoke none of this. He stared at Dermot, and Dermot stared back, and then the moon came out.

Ben Bulben is a mountain like a table. It rises, massive, from the plain, but its summit is flat as a plank. And there, on the top of the table, stood the boar. It was the largest, wildest boar Dermot had ever seen. It was worth the hunt.

He raced up the hill towards it, the Fianna at his heels. They saw him hit the boar with his sword, heard the clang, saw the broken blade clatter down the hill. Dermot's other sword was out, in his hand, as he ran. He chased the boar until it turned, cornered. He jumped onto its back, and drove the sword in, hard through the leathery hide. The boar squealed and bucked, trying to throw him off, but Dermot still hung on.

The boar charged down the hillside, recklessly fast, trying to tip off the man who rode its back. Grimly,

Dermot clung on, driving the sword in, again, and again. No boar could last for ever. If he could stay on, add to the wounds, the time must come when the boar would weaken and then die.

It fell. Its front hoof hit against a root, and it twisted onto the ground. Dermot was thrown over its head, and he ran to strike its head just as the boar twisted its tusk, goring Dermot's side. As he watched the old boar die, he held his hand to his side, but he knew the blood would gush out nonetheless.

MacCool, slower than he used to be, arrived. He stood leaning against a tree, panting, and nodded at the body of the boar.

'You're the champion of all hunters.'

'I'm dead, unless you save me.'

MacCool shrugged. 'But how can I do that?'

'You know. You have the power. If you bring water from a mountain spring, then you can save my life.'

MacCool knew all right. He was not sure that Dermot knew, but he could not deny the truth. The Fianna gathered, breathless from the chase, and they saw the hunter and his prey.

'It's a pity there's no stream here.'

'But there is, MacCool. It's here.'

Dermot's old friends pointed, and MacCool moved across, slower than he need, towards the stream. Dermot was gasping, pleading, as Finn put his palms together, and gathered the pure, clear water that could save his enemy's life. Halfway across the clearing, he stumbled.

When they talked it about later, the Fianna could not agree whether or not he tripped, but the ground was flat and there were no roots there.

Finn MacCool, mighty hero, leader of the Fianna, felt a chill of shame. This was not worthy of him. He was a great man, and he could forgive. Dermot, the boar-slayer, needed his help, and all the world would see that he was man enough to give it. Faster now, he returned to the spring, filled his hands with water, but as he turned to Dermot he saw the hands drop down, the blood gush out and the body drop to the ground. The beautiful Gronnia would gather her children, comfort them, and wait for her husband's return, but she would wait in vain.

And now, at the foot of Ben Bulben, travellers will find a special place. There is a cave there, and even today, children are taught that this was the final rest for Dermot and Gronnia, lovers who for love were forced to run away, in search of the one home they could find.

Notes on Poor Man's Reward

Like many folktales, this story combines realistic everyday settings with fantastic events. Stories like this one, where an outsider in one community becomes a hero in another, are found in cultures all over the world.

Myths and legends often deal with patterns such as 'there were three brothers' or 'she had three wishes'.

Just to be different, this story has a pattern of four, but each time the man does a creature a favour, we know that somewhere that favour will be returned.

What do you think?
In real life very few people have this rags-to-riches experience. So how do you account for the popularity of stories like this one?

Questions
1. What do the poor man's encounters with the four creatures have in common?
2. Why does the king not give his daughter to the poor man as soon as he has succeeded in picking her out?
3. Part of our enjoyment of the story relies on our ability to appreciate its patterns. This might be summed up as *failure – four good deeds – four tests – success*. At what point were you able to predict how the story might end?

Poor Man's Reward

Once there was a young man who was very poor. His parents had died when he was only a boy and he was brought up by his grandparents. But now they were dead, too, and he was lonely and unhappy. He had no cattle, no fine clothes, no valuable belongings, and because of this the people of his village ignored him.

One day, the poor man decided he had had enough of his unfriendly village. He would set off – it didn't matter where – to see if he'd have better luck in another part of the country.

He packed all the food he had left – a small amount of meat, millet and honey – in a bag and filled a small calabash with water. Very early next morning, before anyone else in the village was stirring, he set off towards the east.

He walked for miles across the dusty plain and by the middle of the day he was hot and tired. Luckily there was a tree nearby so he sat under it and rested in the shade. Feeling hungry he opened his bag and took out some millet wrapped in a cloth. Just then he heard a voice above him.

'I'm starving. Could I have some of your millet?'

He looked up and there was a weaverbird perched on a branch. It looked thin and bedraggled. Astonished that the bird could talk the man replied, 'Of course you can,' and stretched up the millet so that the bird could peck at the grain. There was only a little bit left at the bottom when the bird had finished.

'Thank you,' said the weaverbird. 'I won't forget your kindness.'

The man ate the rest of the millet and went on his way. He walked until dark and then climbed into a tree to sleep. In the morning he set off again and at midday once more he sat down in the shade of a tree to shelter from the burning sun. This time he thought he would eat the meat and just as he was pulling out a hunk he heard something scratching the ground behind him. He looked around and there was a scrawny-looking hyena eyeing the meat.

'Excuse me,' it said, 'but do you think you could spare the bones when you've finished the meat? You see, I haven't eaten for two days and I'm feeling a little peckish.'

The man could hardly believe his eyes. Here was a hyena, standing right beside him and talking most politely to him. He could see drops of saliva forming at the edge of the hyena's mouth and realized that it was ravenously hungry. He decided to share his meal.

'Hold on a minute, I'll just take a mouthful or two and then you can have the rest.'

The hyena crouched patiently beside the man and in no time at all a big bone, still with plenty of meat attached to it, was placed by its front paws. It ripped off the meat and swallowed it in a few gulps. Then it settled down to gnaw the bone. The man stood up to go.

'Oh! Sorry!' said the hyena. 'I was enjoying my meal so much I nearly forgot to say thank you. But I won't forget your kindness.'

The man trekked on, his feet sore and his face burning from the heat of the sun. At dusk he found a tree to sleep in and the following morning he started off early, with only the honey and the water left in his bag.

At midday his legs were aching and he sat down to rest by some bushes. He took out a small gourd filled with honey, dipped his fingers in and scooped some out. As the delicious sweetness slid down his throat he began to feel much better and was just helping himself to more when he heard something buzzing round his head and then a tiny voice said, 'I'd love some of that. There isn't any nectar for miles around.'

It was a bee. This time, the man wasn't surprised to hear an animal talking. He felt sorry for the hungry creature and immediately stretched out the gourd so that it could help itself. The bee had a good feed and then flew up to the man's head and piped, 'Thank you, sir, I won't forget your kindness.'

Later that afternoon, feeling dry and dusty, the man stopped to have a drink. Just as he lifted the gourd to his lips he heard a deep, husky voice coming from the grasses behind him.

'Water. Just a sip. Parched.'

The man turned round and jumped backwards when he saw a large, mud-caked crocodile, its tongue hanging out between its long, fearsome teeth.

'Lost my way. Need drink. Now.'

Not very polite, thought the man, but it certainly had lost its way and it did look very dried out. Nervously he walked up to the gaping jaws and held out the gourd.

'Open wide,' he said, 'I'll give you a drink.'

He poured most of the contents of the gourd into the huge mouth. The crocodile gulped noisily.

'Thanks,' it rasped. 'Won't forget your kindness.'

Then it slowly crawled away, its tongue no longer lolling out. As he walked along, the man thought to himself, Well, my luck certainly hasn't changed yet. I've no food left, just a dribble of water and there's no sight of any town or settlement where I could try my fortune.

Just then he spotted a man on the side of a hill and he climbed up to talk to him. The man greeted him in a friendly way and told him that this part of the country belonged to a king who was very wealthy. In fact, his palace was just on the other side of the hill. The stranger suggested that he should go there without delay because the king was offering his daughter to any man who could pick her out in a crowd of people. It wasn't as easy as it sounded, he explained, because the princess had been brought up, with several other girls, in a distant palace, and nobody knew what any of them looked like.

The man thanked the stranger and carried on up the hill. When he reached the top he looked down and saw, below him, a large village with a magnificent palace at one end of it. As he reached the outskirts he could hear the babble of many voices and when he made his way to the meeting place he found that it was packed with people. And strangers, like himself, were arriving and joining the crowd every few minutes.

There seemed to be a wall of faces in front of him. How was he going to be able to move around and see all the young girls? What would a princess look like anyway? Looking down at his dusty, shabby clothes he felt disheartened. Even if he could pick her out, she wouldn't want him.

People were shouting excitedly and the young man felt hot and bothered. On top of everything, an insect was buzzing round his head and he couldn't get rid of it. Suddenly he heard a familiar voice.

'Don't worry,' it piped, 'it's only me, the bee you helped a few days ago. Now it's my turn to help you. Stand on that bank over there and watch me. I'll fly to a girl and pretend to sting her. She'll probably throw her arms in the air and try to brush me away. Once you've seen her I'll fly off. Go and claim her then – she's the king's daughter.'

Before the man had time to thank the bee, it led him to a grassy bank and then flew back into the crowd. He lost sight of it but in a moment he saw a girl frantically waving her arms about. He made straight for her and as he got near she stopped waving. Now he could see that she was very beautiful. He hesitated and then went up to her and said,

'You are the king's daughter.'

The girl nodded and the word went through the crowd

that she had been claimed. The king came up but when he saw how poor the man was, he suddenly said, 'Yes, yes, this is my daughter, but of course you must realize, that's not all you have to do to win her. There are tasks – many of them – and you must complete them all before you can marry her.'

Then he announced the second task: the man was to sort out a heap of mixed seeds, containing millet, maize and sorghum, into separate piles. When he showed him the size of the heap – a hill of seeds that nearly filled half the courtyard – and told him that it was to be finished by morning, the man shook his head in silence. How could he possibly do it in just one night?

He was sitting down, with his head between his hands, when a small bird alighted on his shoulder.

'Hello, friend,' it said. 'Can I be of any help?'

The man was delighted to see the weaverbird again and explained his problem. The bird cocked its head on one side for a minute and then chirped, 'I'll be back in a minute. Don't go away.'

The man sat patiently, wondering what the little bird was up to. Then he saw what looked like a grey cloud above the palace roof, moving towards him. As it rolled closer he could make out hundreds of weaverbirds and they were all heading for the courtyard. They landed on the ground and before he had time to work out what was happening, they delved into the pile, picked up the seeds, one by one, and carried them, in their beaks, to the other side of the courtyard.

'We're good at this sort of thing,' the weaverbird explained as the man watched the three new piles growing steadily and the hill shrinking. Before the first cock started to crow they had finished and they flew off, in a flock, over the palace roof. The man shouted, 'Thank you' after them.

When the king's servants arrived at daybreak, the man was standing, grinning, in front of the piles. They reported the scene to the king who rushed into the courtyard and stared at the unexpected sight.

'Indeed,' he muttered, 'yes … yes … well of course that's only the second task. There'll be another one this evening.'

He swept out of the courtyard and the man wondered what might be in store for him this time. Later that day he saw the servants killing a bull and boiling it in a huge pot. When he went to the palace in the evening the king told him that his task for the night was to eat all the meat of the cooked bull, right down to the bones.

When the man took his first few mouthfuls he was hungry and thought it would be easy enough to eat all the meat. But soon he felt stuffed and couldn't face another bite. There was still a mountain of meat on the ground in front of him. All of a sudden he spotted the bright eyes of an animal creeping towards the carcass. As it drew closer he could make out the shape of a hyena. He looked around to see where he could hide when he heard a voice.

'Don't be frightened, kind sir, it's only me, the hyena you fed out on the plains. What are you doing here?'

As the man explained about his impossible task a big smile spread across the hyena's face.

'Allow me to make a suggestion,' it said, when the man had finished. 'Let me fetch my family and we will have no trouble dealing with this little problem of yours. Just you wait and see.'

The hyena disappeared but returned in just a few minutes with several hungry-looking hyenas. They wasted no time and, positioning themselves all round the carcass, tore off every bit of meat until all that was left was a pile of bones. The man couldn't believe his luck: three impossible tasks and he had achieved them all, thanks to the animals.

The next morning, the astonished king, realizing that he could not go on setting this man tasks for ever, announced that this would be the last one. Confident that the man couldn't possibly be successful with this one, he stood in the meeting place and addressed the people.

'On the other side of our wide river there is a magical ostrich feather. This man must cross the river in broad daylight and return with the feather. Then he can marry my daughter and become king when I die.'

The crowd fell silent for a moment and then, talking in whispers, followed the man down to the river. When he stood on the bank he realized why the crowd had grown so quiet. Breaking the surface of the muddy water were the bulging eyes and lashing tails of hundreds of crocodiles. It was a terrifying sight.

All of a sudden the man felt as if his feet were bolted to the ground. He could not move. If he went forwards he would certainly be killed, if he stepped backwards he would lose the king's daughter who was standing further up the bank, gazing at him admiringly. A deep voice interrupted his thoughts.

'Here. At your feet. Got a problem?'

There was the crocodile he had helped, looking much happier than before. The man told him what his final task was.

'Problem?' it said. 'No problem. You see. Kind man,' and with a swish of its tail it disappeared underwater.

The man stared at the river as, with much splashing and thrashing, the crocodiles gathered together in the centre. Then, as if they'd been given an order, they formed a straight line right in front of him from bank to bank, each crocodile holding the tail of the one in front.

'Step across,' said the man's friend who was once more at his feet. 'Bridge of crocodiles.'

As the man stepped on to the crocodile's back the crowd start to clap and shout. Even the king was impressed. The man was so excited he walked faster and faster over the living bridge until he reached the other side. He picked up the ostrich feather, which was sticking out of the ground, and jumped back on to the crocodiles' backs. He felt as if he were walking on air. When he stepped off, he turned and thanked his crocodile friend.

'Any time,' replied the crocodile and it sank back under

the water until all that the man could see were its huge eyes. The people crowded round to congratulate him as he made his way up to the king and his daughter.

'There's no doubt about it, you're a remarkable man,' said the king. 'Welcome to my family.'

The princess smiled in agreement and the poor young man knew that his lonely days were gone for ever.

Notes on Balder

In this Scandinavian story from Norse mythology we have to imagine that the universe is divided into three:

- Asgard, home of the gods, also known as Valhalla
- Midgard, the earth
- Niflhel ('mist-world'), a dark, cold place, where giants and evil dwarves lived, along with the souls of the dead.

The Norse myths are probably not as well known in Britain as Greek and Roman ones, but we do have a link with them through the names of some of our days of the week: Tiw's day; Woden's day, (Woden was also called Odin, as he is in this story) and Thor's day

The people who listened to these stories believed that the earth would come to an end when the giants and demons from the lower world attacked and overcame the gods. This is why the character of Loki (who appears in many Norse myths) is important. Although he lives with the gods he resents their power and tries to undermine them, as he does in this story. In Norwegian folktales, Loki appears as a fire-demon – and some Norwegians still say when the fire crackles, 'Loki is thrashing his children'.

What do you think?

Sometimes you need to concentrate on the sound of a story to know what's going on. In *Balder* there's a beat that suggests this is a big important story stretching from heaven to hell.

See if you can find some moments where the rhythm of the sentences helps draw you into the drama.

Questions

1. The twins Balder and Hodur are opposites in more ways than one. How are the contrasts between them important to the story?
2. How do Odin and Frigga react differently to Balder's dreams and fears?
3. Why do you think Loki wants to destroy Balder?
4. What effects does Frigga fear Balder's death will have beyond Valhalla?
5. What conclusion do you draw from the sombre ending of this story?

Balder

In the cold, mountain country of the North, that we now call Scandinavia, Asgard was the kingdom of the gods. King of the gods was Odin, who had fought against the giants of the frost. Thanks to him, the land had been rescued from their grip, and their great enemy Ymir had been killed. Out of Ymir's corpse they had made the world, the ocean from his blood, cliffs from his teeth and trees and vegetation from his hair.

Odin was a tall and strong, with a grey beard. He sat on his throne, with the two ravens, Hugin and Mnin, on his shoulders. Each day they would fly off, gather the news, and return to him before dark. At his feet were his two hunting hounds, that Odin fed with the meat from his plate. He ate nothing himself, but lived on wine.

Frigga the queen, was tall and beautiful, and dressed in white. She had a palace of her own, and a mind of her own, and, when she needed to be, could be cleverer than the king. But she loved him, and was faithful to him, and the other gods looked up to Odin and Frigga, sure of their love and proud of their king and queen. When they heard that Frigga was expecting another child, they celebrated, and prepared to greet the new prince.

Frigga had twin boys, and they were as different as it was possible for two boys to be. Hodur was gloomy and blind, with no light in his eyes and darkness in his soul.

Balder was the child of light, bright, cheerful, and with perfect skin. Everyone who saw the baby Balder praised his happy face, his golden hair, and walked away smiling. He was the hope of the world.

Balder grew up wise and sensitive. He might seem too good to be true, but even those who came to sneer were charmed by his good nature and intelligence. He knew the skill of reading runes, the properties of herbs, and what each flower could do. The camomile, whose white flower was as smooth and pure as his forehead, became known as 'Balder's brow'. All that could be known at that time Balder understood. The one thing he could not see was the fate that lay in wait for him.

Balder married Nanna, who was young and beautiful, and seemed to have everything. But his mother Frigga noticed that he looked concerned. His confidence was seeping away, like water from an aging cask. The smile came more slowly, and was quicker to fade. There was a shadow in his mind.

'What troubles you, my son?'

'I have no troubles. I have Nanna, and my life ahead of me.' He held his mother's hand. 'What should I have to fear?'

In turn, she gripped his shoulders, and stared into his face. 'Balder, I am not a fool. I read your mind. What troubles you?'

He turned away and laughed, but only for a moment. Then he sat down. 'No, I cannot lie to you. I have these dreams.'

She sat beside him. 'Tell me, my son.'

'There is little to tell. Weird creatures, like nothing we have seen. No sense, no reason for concern. But when I wake, I am afraid.'

'But what do you fear? Balder, what could you fear?'

'That is what frightens me, mother. I do not know.'

Frigga was concerned, and went to Odin. He was uneasy and, like her, determined that nothing should harm their son. But he also, king of the gods, was afraid. For both of them this was a new sensation, like freezing rain, sinking into their clothes, but they responded in different ways.

Frigga sent out her servants, in different directions, between them covering the land. Their mission was to register a vow. Each animal, each bird, each plant must swear, that they would cause no harm to Balder. Even the mountains and the rocks must promise that no harm would come to him. And they swore, happily, for there was nothing on earth which did not love Balder, who was warm and radiant as the sun.

At the end of a tiring day one of the servants returned to the palace. He had just passed the entrance to Valhalla, when he remembered that he had forgotten to speak to the mistletoe that grew on the stump of an oak. But mistletoe was a small, soft plant with a berry, that could do nobody harm, and he was weary and ready for his bed. Surely it couldn't matter, after a long day's work and a good job done.

111

Odin, meanwhile, was in pursuit of the truth. On his huge eight-footed horse, the mighty Sleipnir, he galloped through Helgate, into Hel, the region of the dead. He was surprised to find a table spread with food, and couches covered with gold. Such preparations were not for any ordinary guest.

Odin chanted a magic spell, and out of the ground rose Vala, one of the prophets of the truth.

'Who are you, that dares to trouble my rest?'

The king of the gods pretended to be a passer-by, interested by the preparation of the feast. Which guest did they expect to entertain?

'Our table is prepared for Balder, god of light. Killed by the forces of the darkness, Balder will come to our feast.'

This was what he expected, what he feared. But Odin did not reveal himself. 'Who will refuse to mourn my son?' he asked.

And the Vala knew that this was no passer-by. Only a god could know what that question might mean. She did not reply, but sank back into the silence of the tomb. Nothing would ever tempt her out again, not until the last day, and the ending of the world.

Odin rode slowly back to Asgard, preparing himself for the time when the brilliance of Balder would shine no more. Frigga greeted him, anxiously, urgently, assuring him that everything in creation had promised that no harm would come to their son. Odin nodded, said nothing and tried to force a smile, but the prophecy of the Vala still echoed in his ears.

Frigga and Odin had done all that they could to protect their son. Glad that the threat to Balder had passed, the gods relaxed. On Idavold, the playground of the gods, they competed in sports, each trying to hurl golden disks further than the other. Then they devised a new game.

When a strong man invites us to hit him in the chest, we are jealous, because we would not say the same to him. We are impressed, by his strength and courage. But we are also angry and aroused, to see whether or not we can make him hurt. In the same way, the gods made up a game to test whether Balder's protection was complete.

They threw things at him, spears and rocks and spars of wood, missiles which would have injured any of them. But the things, which had vowed never to harm Balder, fell short, or missed him, or bounced away to safety. The gods watched each other fail, laughing and cheering as they watched.

Frigga was busy spinning in Fensalir, when she thought she saw an old woman passing by. In fact, it was Loki the mischiefmaker, travelling in disguise, so that even the queen of the gods was fooled.

'What is that noise?' Frigga asked.

'The gods are at their sports,' the woman answered. 'They're throwing everything at Balder, but nothing seems to hurt. It's strange.'

'Not at all,' Frigga replied. 'It is exactly what I should expect.'

'Why so?' she asked, and the old woman moved closer, clutching her shawl tightly around her, but the queen continued spinning.

'The whole of creation loves the light. Balder is the sun, who smiles upon them; they love him, and have sworn to do him no harm.' Loki seethed as he heard these words, for he had always done harm, and creatures who saw him coming were keen to keep out of his way. But his hatred did not show.

'Tell me, your highness, has everything sworn? Each creature, each rock, each plant?'

'Of course,' she smiled. 'Well, all except one. My servant forgot the mistletoe, but that's a soft and harmless parasite. So I don't think Balder's much to fear, do you?'

The old woman bowed, and edged to the door. 'Indeed, your majesty, the beloved Balder seems to have all he wants. And which of us could be so lucky, eh?' she cackled, and hobbled away, while Frigga continued to spin.

Once out of sight of Fensalir, Loki became himself again, and ran to Valhalla's gate. He found the oak stump, ripped the mistletoe from it, and worked such magic on the soft, green plant that it became a dart, thin and hard. He spat on a berry, and moulded it with his fingers, into a point as sharp as flint. Hiding the dart in his cloak, he returned to Idavold.

The young gods had still not tired of their game. Balder was in the middle, laughing louder than anyone, as the stream of missiles plopped softly to the ground. Standing apart, leaning on a tree, was his brother Hodur.

'Hodur,' Loki asked, 'Is something wrong?'

'The whole world loves my brother. What should be wrong?'

'You sound bitter.'

Hodur said nothing, but spat on the ground.

Loki was not put off. 'You're not taking part in the game?'

'I'm not in the mood for games. And besides, you know I'm blind.'

'Well, if that is all that stops you. Here ...' Gently, kindly, Loki guided Hodur until he was facing the target. He placed the dart in Hodur's hand. 'Now, take your arm back, and ... throw!'

Helpless, angry, blind, he threw the dart. He turned, to accept the laughter and the jeers of the gods, as he too failed with them. But there was nothing. No sound at all. A terrible silence fell over Idavold, as the gods watched Balder fall, clutch at the dart in pain, and then lie there still. They had covered over their fears and doubts, welcomed Frigga's precautions and Odin's ride, used the game and the laughter of their friends to reassure themselves. But all that now was torn away, like a tent in a storm. The prophecy had been fulfilled. Balder was dead.

The gods had sworn not to desecrate their home with violence, but Hodur's crime made that an easy promise to break. Sensing their hatred, his arms stretched out, to feel for the companion who had shown him where to throw. But by this time, his mischief achieved, Loki was long gone. Balder's brother, miserable and blind, stood alone.

He was the one who had thrown the dart, and he must pay.

'Stop!' Frigga's voice, normally so calm, shrilled with tears. 'You think I wish to lose both sons? Balder is gone. The glory of my days is overcast, and murder is your way to put it right?' She glared round at them, deepening their shame. But what else could they do?

'I want him back.' Uneasily, they shifted, looking from one, to the other. Queen of the gods or not, this was a mother maddened by grief. The dead do not return.

'I want him back. All earth, the whole creation, needs my son. Gods, you call yourselves. Well, act like gods. Go to the region of the dead, bargain with Hel, and bring me back the brightness of my son.' Nobody moved. Nobody spoke. A fool's errand, but who is brave enough to call the queen a fool?

Odin moved quietly to her side. 'There are rewards. My horse Sleipnir stands by, ready to bear the messenger. Whoever rides to Hel will earn our love, greater than any of the gods.' He looked round. He had offered all he had, but still their faces were uneasy. They looked at each other or stared at the ground, hoping that a voice would speak.

'I shall go.' Hermod, Balder's elder brother, stepped forward. He bowed to Frigga, his mother, and Odin led him to where Sleipnir stood. None but Odin had ever ridden him, and the huge horse neighed, clattering across the path. The king steadied him, whispered in his ear, and held the reins as Hermod leapt into the saddle. Odin handed him the reins, slapped Sleipnir's rump, and horse and rider vanished in the dust.

Odin sent Balder's body to be dressed, and ordered the gods to cut down trees. Huge pines were chopped into pieces, and taken down to the shore. On Balder's ship, Ringhorn, a vast bonfire was built. It was decorated with tapestries and flowers, rings and ornaments, weapons and precious stones. And finally the body of his son, washed and dressed in a golden robe; was laid upon the pyre.

The gods gathered round. Slowly, one at a time, they came forward to say their farewells. As his wife Nanna bent over Balder's body, she sobbed, and shook, and fell to the deck. They rushed forward, and reached to help her stand, but there was nothing they could do. Her heart was broken, she was with Balder, and they laid her by his side. They placed the thorns of sleep around the wood, and prepared to launch the ship.

Then Odin stepped forward, and whispered in his dead son's ear. None heard the words he spoke, but they saw him take off his magic ring, Draupnir, and add it to the offerings by the pyre. He stepped back, and signalled to the gods to launch the ship.

They leaned their shoulders against it, and they pushed with all their might. Nothing happened. So heavy was the load of fuel, so rich the treasures they had piled on, that the ship could not be moved. The mountain giants looked on, and asked for the help of the giantess Hyrrrokin. She came, riding on a massive wolf, which she controlled with a bridle made of snakes.

She looked at the ship, then round at the gods with

scorn. She challenged them to hold her wolf, got off, and stood at the stern of the ship. She firmly fixed her feet, set her shoulder against it, and heaved. The timbers creaked, she strained again and then the ship shot into the sea. The pine tree rollers smoked as the keel shrieked across them, and Thor leapt into the ship to light the fire.

He jumped out into the shallows, and rejoined the gods, to watch the great ship drifting out to sea. The flames licked into the sky, and as the vessel moved towards the west it seemed as though the horizon had vanished. The sea and the sky were one, melted in a blaze of fire, orange, pink and red, and the gods watched until the vessel sank, and the embers died, and Balder's light was smothered by the dark.

For ten days Hermod rode, till he reached the bridge at Giallar, which trembled as he crossed. Then Modgud barred his way.

'What is your business here? Why are you, a living man, riding to the world of Hel?'

'My business concerns Balder and Nanna. Have they passed this way?'

'They have crossed the bridge,' she said, 'and you may cross over, knowing that, from now on, you ride down and north, a huge barrier no man could ever cross. Even Sleipnir whinnied with fear. Slowly, Hermod got off. He walked round the horse, tightening the girths, whispering in his

118

ear.

'Yes, Sleipnir, it is a mighty gate. But we have come far, and it is Odin's work we do. For Balder, believe me, we can fly.' And it seemed that Sleipnir whinnied in reply. Hermod remounted, walked the horse back away from the gate, then turned him with great deliberation, urged him on with the reins and dug his spurs deep into his sides. He felt his weight, the horse's weight lift steadily into the air like some great bird, and in seconds they had cleared the gate.

On he rode, till he came to the banqueting hall. There was Balder, sitting on a bench, with Nanna beside him. They were pale, as ghosts.

'Balder, I have come to take you back.'

Sadly, slowly, his brother shook his head. 'I must remain, until the last day. But take back Nanna, who does not deserve to die.'

'I am with you, Balder, in life or death. Do not ask me to live without you. If you stay here, I too shall remain.'

[text obscured by smudge] the brightest sun of all is dead return. All [text obscured] him back, longed for his [text obscured] Hel, his messenger cried, 'If you help, we all [text obscured] world [text obscured] am free.

[text obscured] said Loki, 'He can stay in Hel. The [text obscured] th?

[text obscured] weep for Balder now.'

'Very well.' Hermod felt a chill wind sweep through the banqueting hall, as Hel allowed herself a smile. 'We shall

119

see. If all things, all creatures, shed their tears, then they may have their Balder back.'

Hermod waited, for the catch. He knew the grief he had left behind, the relief that would flow if Balder might return. Could it be this easy? Was this the end of the task that had frightened the bravest of the gods? Trying to hide a smile, he thanked Hel solemnly, and turned to go. Balder handed him Draupnir, their father's ring, and wished him well.

Back in Asgard they waited for his news. As soon as he arrived, and gasped out Hel's demands, messengers were sent to all corners of the earth. Each animal and bird, each rock and tree, wept in their own way, that Balder should return. All creation was awash with grief, a flood of tears to warm the coldest heart.

Except one. Near Asgard was a dark cave, and hiding in its shadows was the dark figure of a woman, who was Loki in disguise.

'Will you mourn the death of light?' they called.

The woman laughed.

'Balder, our god, the brightest sun of all, is dead.'

'So, let him die.'

'He is in Hel', the messenger cried. 'If you help, we all help, we can set him free.'

'For all I care', said Loki, 'He can stay in Hel.' The messenger did not give up. He pleaded, argued and threatened, but to no effect. Nothing could reach the heart of Loki, colder than any stone.

Back at the palace, Odin and Frigga were smiling. As

each messenger brought news of the great mourning, the flood of tears, growing by the day, so their hearts lifted and their eyes were bright. They began to believe that they would see their son again. Only one messenger was still to return, and the gods went down, to greet him on the road. They cheered as they saw him in the distance, but as he got closer the cheers died in the air. He did not need to speak. His face said plainly, that he had found a creature, only one, who would not weep for Balder. But one was enough. And so Odin and Frigga saw that their precious son was lost to them, and to all creation, his brilliance buried in the dark until the end of time.

Notes on The Death of Gelert

Visitors to Snowdonia will know the small town of Beddgelert ('Gelert's Grave') and may well have seen the monument recording this story.

What do you think?
Like many legendary heroes, Llewellyn faces danger and disaster. In what ways though is his story unusual?

Question
1. Ballads began as an oral form of poetry – heard rather than read – and therefore needed to have a strong storyline and to be memorable so that they could be passed on by word of mouth. In this modern version of an old legend, the writer has used many of the features of a traditional ballad:

- repetition, of sounds and words
- snatches of dialogue to move the story along
- suspense/surprise
- strong images (look especially at how verbs are used at dramatic moments)
- metaphor
- regular rhythm (a strong ti-tum, ti-tum beat)
- regular rhymes (ABCB in each four lined verse).

See if you can find an example of each of these and talk about what it contributes to the telling of the story.

The Death of Gelert

Llewellyn was a mighty prince
Of stature and renown,
Beneath the might of Snowdon's peak
No finer could be found.

All huntsmen knew his speed and strength,
All robbers feared his sword
And all men counted it a boast
To follow such a lord.

'Rise up, good friends, prepare yourselves
And blow the hunting horn,
We'll chase the fastest deer we find
Until tomorrow's dawn.'

'But who will guard your heir, my son
While hounds and horses run?'
'I'll leave behind my favourite hound
He'd die to save my son.'

Sure of his home, he saddled up
And left without delay
While Gelert from the doorway watched
His master ride away.

The sun rose up the following day,
The sky was bright and clear
As from the castle all could see
The weary band appear.

Then down the steps to greet his lord
Did eager Gelert race
But with what dread his master felt
The blood upon his face.

Llewellyn leapt the flight of stairs
He thundered through the door
A blood-stained pile of blankets lay
All scattered on the floor.

The huntsman could not see his son
The cot was overturned,
The blood that dripped from Gelert's jaws
Upon his fingers burned.

'Ungrateful cur' Llewellyn roared
'My service to betray!'
Within a trice his sword had struck
And Gelert lifeless lay.

The hound had barely breathed his last,
The sword had been put by
When with a shock his master heard
A faint, a whimpered cry.

In disbelief he tracked the sound
Beneath the gory pile,
To where his happy infant son
Beheld him with a smile.

Slowly, the father raised the clothes
His blood to ice had chilled,
For there, beneath the blankets, lay
The wolf that Gelert killed.

'Oh, Gelert, there are wicked men
That roam these hillsides free
But none have done so foul a thing
As I have done to thee.'

Llewellyn left the castle then
And walked for many a mile
But from that day until his death
None ever saw him smile.

Notes on Anansi and the Mind of God

Anansi is one of those trickster figures who crop up in other stories in this collection. (See *Whose Footprints?* and *How Coyote Stole Fire*). As in *Balder* and *The Death of Gelert*, the rhythm is an important way of moving the story along. Here it's a happy, cheeky beat, almost like a rap.

What do you think?

It seems as though people have always liked the idea that rules are there to be broken and that even the most powerful beings can be challenged by the daring and cleverness of creatures like Anansi. There is certainly a power struggle going on in this story. Who do you want to win? Why?

Questions

1. How does Anansi react to the impossible task God sets him?

2. What plan does he come up with to find the information he needs?

3. How does Anansi gain an advantage over God at the end of the story?

4. What do you think God and Anansi have in common?

5. In what ways are they different?

Anansi and the Mind of God

Anansi was an African. Spider-man Anansi. But he stowed away on a slave ship to the West Indies, so now he turns up in Jamaica and suchlike, as sneaky as a tarantula in a hand of bananas. Spider-man Anansi, Anansi the Trickster. They do say Anansi's the cleverest creature next to God … or was it Anansi said that?

Now Spider-man Anansi was a clever man,
But he got to boasting he was God's right hand.
Said God, 'Anansi, if you're really so smart,
You can tell what I'm thinking in my heart of hearts.
There's three things I want, and if you're my peer,
You'll have no trouble in fetching them here.'
Well, Spider-man Anansi, he up and fled,
Swinging down from Heaven on his long black thread.
He ain't one clue what he's s'pose' to fetch back,
But he ain't gonna let God Almighty know that.
He seeks out the birdies, one, two, three;
Says, 'Spare one feather for Mister Anansi!'
Asks every bird for just one feather,
Then Anansi-man, he sews them together.

He sews him a glorious rainbow suit:
Feather pyjamas, feather mask and boots,
Then off he flies high up in the sky,
And he dances about till he takes God's eye.
God says, 'Well Lordy, and upon my word!

Who's gonna tell me 'bout this rainbow bird?
I know I didn't make it, so who else did?'
And he asked the mack'rel and he asked the squid.
He asked the turtle and he asked the dog,
And he asked the monkey and he asked the frog,
And he asked the bird, but it just jumped by,
Giving out a perfume like a rainbow pie.

Now God's advisors racked their brains all day,
But they couldn't find but one thing to say:
'Anansi's the man who could solve this case.'
Says God, 'But I sent *him* on a wild-goose chase!
I sent him to fetch three things to me:
So I fear that's the end of old Anansi.'
'Why? What did you send him for, Lord?' ask they.
'For the night and the moon and the light of day.
Not that I said so. No, I made him guess,
'Cos he got to boasting he was better than best.
But now he's gone, well, I'm sorry, kinda –
That I told Anansi to be a read-minder.'
All the creatures laughed, but God wasn't luffin',
When away flew the bird like a shaggy puffin.

It was no sooner gone than who comes in,
But Spider Anansi in his own black skin.
In came Anansi with a bulging sack.
Says, 'Sorry I kept you, Lord, but now I'm back.
Anansi-man's back and I think you'll find
I've brought you the three things were on your mind.'

So he reaches in the sack and oh! what a fright,
He plunges Heaven into darkest night.
Out comes the moon next with a silv'ry shine
And God says, 'Mercy me, I thought I'd gone blind!
Touché, Anansi-man, you got me licked.
I don't know how, but I know I been tricked.'
Then Anansi pulls out the great big sun –
All its terrible bright illu-min-a-tion,
And it burns God's eyeball in a place or two,
And it gives him pain, and it spoils his view.

So when God looks down now from his throne on high
There's a patch he misses with his sun-scorched eye.
You can bet that Spider-man knows where it be –
That patch of ground God Almighty can't see.

Is that where you're hiding, Mister Anansi?

Notes on Pandora's Box

In this Greek myth, Pandora is created by the gods as part of a plot to get revenge on the Titan, Prometheus. The gods were very concerned that the Titans, a race of giants with superhuman powers, should not be allowed to get above themselves. Zeus was particularly keen to punish Prometheus for stealing fire from the sun and giving it to human beings.

What do you think?
In the original version of the story, the box was a vase and Pandora brought it with her when the gods sent her to earth. In this modern version, the box belongs to her husband and some of the things that come out of it couldn't possibly have happened to the ancient Greeks.

After reading the story think about:

- which of the escaping problems could belong to any time and which are specifically modern
- whether changing the ending (from 'vase sent by the gods' to 'husband's box') makes a difference to the way you react to Pandora.

Questions
1. What are the characteristics of the Titans?
2. In what way is Prometheus a typical Titan?
3. In mythologies with many gods rather than one, the gods were often complex characters and far from perfect. What do you think of Zeus behaviour in this story?
4. How far do you think Pandora is to blame for the damage she causes?
5. In earlier versions of the story the contents of the box/vase are usually referred to generally as 'ills' or 'afflictions'. In this version the writer has clearly enjoyed making a long, detailed and not entirely serious list of terrible things. How many of these would be on your personal list? Would you add others?

Pandora's Box

(Zeus, king of the gods, was unhappy at the way that people were behaving. He decided to teach them a lesson.)

First he visited the crippled god Hephaestus who worked at a great forge in Olympus with twenty bellows pumping twenty-four hours a day. Although ugly and misshapen himself, no blacksmith was more skilled than Hephaestus.

'I want you to make me a woman,' the king of the gods commanded. 'I want her to be more beautiful than any woman ever seen on the face of the earth. She must be perfect. As perfect as a goddess.'

Hephaestus did as he was told. He had only ever disobeyed Zeus once. That had been just before he became the crippled god. Now he fashioned a woman out of clay, moulding her perfect features with his own hands. He commissioned the four winds to breathe life into her and asked all the goddesses to help dress her in their finest clothes and jewels.

The result was Pandora.

When Zeus saw the blacksmith-god's work, he was well pleased and instructed Hermes to carry her into the world at once. There she was married to a certain King Epimetheus, the brother of Prometheus and the only other Titan who had not joined in the war against the gods.

Now Epimetheus had been warned never to trust the gifts of Zeus, but seeing the terrible fate that had befallen his brother, he was too afraid to refuse. Moreover, he had to admit that Pandora was beautiful. You'd have had to be mad to think otherwise. When she walked into the room, men fell silent and all eyes turned on her. Whatever she said, people would agree. When she made jokes, the laughter would continue for several minutes. Whatever she did was greeted with applause. And Epimetheus did feel rather proud to be married to her.

Unfortunately, the things Pandora said were never really worth listening to, for she was not a very intelligent creature. Her jokes were in truth extremely unfunny. She did very little because she was impossibly lazy and if Epimetheus was glad to be her husband, she made him a poor and unfaithful wife. For this was the revenge of Zeus. He had made her as shallow and as coquettish as she was beautiful. And she was to cause more trouble to mankind than any woman before or any woman since.

For Epimetheus owned a large, ebony box which was kept in a special room in his palace, guarded day and night. In this box he had collected and imprisoned all the things that could harm mankind. It was the one room in the palace that Pandora was forbidden to enter and naturally it was the one room that most aroused her curiosity.

'I bet you keep all sorts of super things in that big, black box of yours,' she would say in her syrupy voice. 'Why don't you let your little Pandy look inside?'

'It is not for you, my dear,' Epimetheus would reply. 'You should leave well alone.'

'But ...'

'No, no, my love. No one may open the box.'

'Then you don't love me,' Pandora would say, crossing her arms and pouting. 'And I'm not going to love you any more – not ever!'

They had this conversation many times until the day when Pandora couldn't resist her curiosity any longer. For despite everything Epimetheus had told her about the box, she still believed that it contained some special treat that he was holding back from her.

'I'll show him ... the old bossy-boots,' she muttered to herself.

Waiting until Epimetheus was out, she managed to talk her way past the guards and into the room. She had stolen the key from beside his bed and nobody thought to stop her. Was she not, after all, the king's wife and the mistress of the house? Her whole body trembling, she knelt down beside the box. It was smaller and older than she had expected. It was also a little surprising (not to say upsetting) that the padlock which fastened it should be in the shape of a human skull. But she was certain it would contain treasure such as would make all her own diamonds and pearls seem like mere pebbles, treasure that would make her the envy of the world. She turned the key and opened the box ...

... and at once all the spites and problems that Epimetheus had for so long kept locked up, exploded into the world. Old age, hard work, sickness … they flew out in a great cloud of buzzing, stinging, biting insects. It was as if Pandora had accidentally split the atom. One moment she was standing there with a foolish grin on her face. The next she was screaming in the heart of an intense darkness that had, in seconds, stripped her of her beauty and brought her out in a thousand boils.

At that moment, all the things that make life difficult today, streamed out of Pandora's box and into the world:

Old age, hard work, sickness, vice, anger, envy, lust, covetousness, spite, sarcasm, cynicism, violence, intolerance, injustice, infidelity, famine, drought, pestilence, war, religious persecution, apartheid, taxation, inflation, pollution, unemployment, fascism, racism, sexism, terrorism, communism, nepotism, cubism, patriotism, nihilism, totalitarianism, plagiarism, vandalism, tourism, paranoia, schizophrenia, kleptomania, claustrophobia, xenophobia, hypochondria, insomnia, megalomania, narrow-mindedness, thoughtlessness, selfishness, bribery, corruption, censorship, gluttony, pornography, delinquency, vulgarity, bureaucracy, complacency, obesity, acne, diplomatic immunity, traffic congestion, party political broadcasts, urban development, modern architecture, fast food, muzak, dolphinariums, organized crime, advertising, alcoholism, drug addiction, monosodium glutamate, nicotine, nuclear waste, data processing, fanaticism, insanity, drizzle, elephant's-feet-wastepaper-baskets and much, much more.

At the last moment, Epimetheus managed to slam down the lid, by which time only one thing was left in the box: hope. Which is just as well. For with all the problems that Pandora had released into the world, where would we be without it?

Tell Me That Again

Notes on Sir Gawain and the Green Knight

According to legend, Gawain was one of King Arthur's knights at the Round Table. This tale of Gawain's encounter with the Green Knight is based on a very old English poem written in the fourteenth century, in a language called Middle English. No-one knows the name of its author and if you saw it you wouldn't understand much of it because the meaning and spelling of so many of our words have changed since then and even the shape of the letters is different. In this modern version the writer has put himself in the position of Arthur, telling the story that Gawain has told him.

What do you think?
There are a number of patterns in the story, some obvious, some less so. How many can you find and how important do they turn out to have been when you reach the end?

Questions
1. The Green Knight is a terrifying sight but Arthur seems happy to welcome him to the Round Table. Why?
2. Why is Gawain glad to accept the Green Knight's challenge? Why does so much depend upon honouring the bargain he makes with the knight?
3. The castle where Gawain stays offers him both security and dangers. Why?
4. What strengths and weaknesses does Gawain show in the Green Chapel?
5. Why is the green belt so important in the story?

Sir Gawain and the Green Knight

I remember it was at Christmas that year, and colder still at New Year, the snow thick on the ground, the wind icy from the north. But neither the snow nor the wind could dampen our spirits. We were at Camelot and it was New Year's Eve once more. Everyone was gathered for the feasting, the knights all in their places at the Round Table; and my dear Guinevere sitting with all the ladies of the court beneath a great canopy. A blazing fire crackled in the hearth, the ale flowed freely and my harpist played as only he could play. Bercelet lay at my feet, waiting in high hopes for the feasting to begin. The boar's head, apple in his mouth, was carried into the hall, and we all of us pounded the table impatiently; for, as was the custom at Camelot, we knew we could not begin eating until we had heard of some new quest, of some stirring adventure. I waited. We all waited. The knights looked at each other, but no one rose to his feet. Nothing happened. Bercelet licked his lips.

At that moment, from outside in the courtyard, came the clatter of a horse's hooves on the cobbles. The doors of the hall flew open, and before I had time to call for them to be closed, a giant of a man rode in on a towering war-horse that pawed the ground, sides lathered up, tossing its fine head, snorting its fury. The man swept the hall with terrible eyes, wolfish eyes that froze the courage in a man's veins, eyes you could not hold with your own. But it was not the man's eyes that amazed us most, it was not

139

his size either – and I tell you I'd never in my life set eyes on a bigger man – no, it was the colour of him. Green, the man was green from head to foot. Green jerkin, common enough; green cloak, again common enough, you might think – but his head was green, his hands as well. And I swear that his hair, which was as long as mine is now, was green too. The horse was green, and the saddle. He wore no armour, but carried a green axe in one hand and in the other a branch he'd ripped off some holly tree – a sign of peace, but he didn't look very peaceful to me.

He threw the branch to the ground as he spoke. 'And who might be the leader of this motley crew? I'll talk to no one else.' It was a moment or two before I could find my voice.

'Welcome, stranger,' I said. 'Why don't you come and join us?'

'I have not come here to waste my time in feasting. I can do that well enough at home. I have something else in mind. You are King Arthur?'

'I am.'

'Well, King Arthur,' he began, his thunderous voice heavy with sarcasm. 'I have heard all about the so-called bravery of you and your knights. The whole world is talking of little else. I have come all this way from my home in the North Country to find out just how brave you are. Looking about me, I see nothing but a bunch of beardless little boys. Are you quite sure I have come to the right place?'

At this there were howls of protest. 'You may bark loud enough,' he went on, 'but I doubt very much if there's anyone here man enough to accept my challenge. We shall see. We shall see.' And he held out his axe in both hands. 'You see this axe? I will submit myself right now to one blow from this axe, just one blow – but only if, in twelve months and a day from now, I can repay the blow in kind, just one blow. Tit for tat, how's that? There, is that simple enough for you dunderheads?'

I looked about the hall. No one moved a muscle. No one said a word.

'Well, I can see I was wrong,' he laughed. 'I said I saw boys about me. I see only chickens.'

Now my blood was up. I had had enough. 'You've asked for it,' I shouted. 'I'll do it, and with pleasure too. Down off your horse.' It wasn't so brave as it sounds. After all, a man without his head could hardly do you much harm, could he?

Then suddenly Gawain was on his feet beside me. 'No, my Lord,' he said. 'Let me. I'll see to him. I'll shut his big mouth for you, once and for all. I've rested on my laurels long enough. It is time I proved myself fit again to sit round this table.'

'Very well, Gawain,' I replied, more than a little relieved. 'But be careful. Things are not always as they seem.'

With a great laugh, the Green Knight jumped down from his horse. 'So, Arthur, at least you have one man amongst all these boys,' he quipped.

141

'Enough!' cried Gawain, striding across the hall to meet him. Dwarfed but not cowed, he squared up to the Green Knight. 'It will be a promise, a bargain between us,' he said. 'I promise, by my honour as a knight, that I will strike you just once, as you've said; and that in a year's time you can do the same to me – if you're still able to, which I doubt.'

'We shall see,' said the Green Knight, and he handed Gawain his axe. 'You do know which end to hold, don't you?'

'Kneel, you overgrown leek!' Gawain cried, gripping the axe tightly. The Green Knight knelt down and pulled aside his hair, so that his neck was bare. Gawain seemed to be hesitating for a moment.

'Come on then, Gawain, what are you waiting for? Are you frightened of the sight of a little blood? Strike man, strike!' Gawain hesitated no longer. He severed the Green Knight's head clean from his shoulders and sent it rolling across the floor. But there was not a drop of blood, green or red, not a single drop – and no time to wonder at it either, for the Green Knight sprang at once to his feet, picked up his head and vaulted headless on to his horse. It was the severed head under his arm that spoke.

'You have a year and a day, Gawain. I am the Green Knight of the Green Chapel in the Forest of Wirral. You'll find me easily enough. If you do not, then the whole world will know that the great Sir Gawain is a coward and all King Arthur's court with him.' With that, he galloped away out into the snow, leaving the hall silent and aghast behind him. It was some time, I can tell you before any of us felt at all festive.

The seasons passed as they always do, slowly enough for the young, but ever faster for the old. And for poor Gawain too, though still young in body and spirit, the year raced by. The following Michaelmas, I held my court at Caerleon and we had a great feast for Gawain to send him on his way. Lancelot was there, Bors, Gareth and Gaheris, Gawain's brothers, Bedivere and all the others. Even the Archibishop was there to bless him. In hushed silence, Gawain put on his fine gold-inlaid armour. We embraced without a word. Then he turned away from me, mounted Gringolet, his black warhorse and rode off. Few of us thought we would ever see him again.

What happened after this Gawain himself later told us. Impetuous he may have been, but he was never one given to exaggeration or wild imaginings. He rode away from us with a heavy heart that day. He travelled up over the windswept hills of North Wales and down into the forests beyond. It was bitterly cold. The forests were a haven for robbers, savage men who could be hiding anywhere, ready to spring out and ambush any luckless stranger. Some, seeing the star of Logres on Gawain's shield and knowing who he was, let him pass by. Others did not. Time and again, Gawain had to fight them off. Many a cold night he slept out in the open, and many a day passed with no food either for himself or his horse, so that they were both much weakened by the time they came at long last into the Forest of Wirral.

He asked anyone and everyone he met where he might find the Green Chapel, but no one seemed to have even heard of it. He began to despair of ever finding the place in time. On and on he rode, ever deeper into the forest, wading through marsh and mud; until on Christmas Eve, he found himself fording a stream and riding through open parkland towards a fine castle. The drawbridge over the moat was down, so he rode across and knocked at the door.

A porter greeted him with a welcoming smile and invited him to come in. Gringolet was led away for a rub-down, then to a warm, dry stable where there was all the sweet hay and all the clean water he could want. Gawain was brought into the hall to meet his host, the lord of the castle. The moment Gawain set eyes on him, he knew he was in good hands, for everything about the man was courteous and kind, from his honest eyes to his open smile. Gawain told him at once who he was and where he had come from.

'No matter who you are,' said the lord of the castle, clasping his hand, 'you are more than welcome to my home. You need rest, and here you shall have all you need. My castle is your castle. Everything I have is yours for as long as you want to stay.' Gawain could hardly believe his good luck.

Then there began three days of Christmas celebrations.

People flocked to the castle from miles around to meet Gawain, and he was feted royally. Nothing was too much trouble. The lady of the castle, his host's wife, saw to his every need – and she was as beautiful a woman as Gawain had ever met. Never had he enjoyed a Christmas as much as this; but from time to time a shadow came over him as he thought of the dreaded appointment with the Green Knight, now only a few short days away. The happier he was, the less he wanted to die.

'You are sad, Gawain,' said the lady of the castle, as they sat talking together late one evening.

'After all you have done for me, my lady, I have no right to be,' Gawain replied. He had tried so hard to drive away his black and fearful thoughts, to hide from them his growing anxiety. 'But I am afraid that tomorrow I shall have to leave and be on my way. I have promised to be at the Green Chapel on New Year's Day, and as yet I don't even know where the place is. I must not be late, I cannot be.'

'Nor shall you be,' laughed the lord of the castle, 'because the Green Chapel you speak of is no more than a two-hour ride from here, on a good horse. And Gringolet is a fine warhorse. So why don't you stay here for three more days, until the morning of New Year's Day itself? I shall have someone show you the way, just to be sure. How would that be?'

'That,' said Gawain, greatly relieved, 'that would make me the happiest man alive. You've been so good to me, so kind. I won't get in the way, I promise. I'll do anything you say everything you say.'

'Well then,' said the lord of the castle, 'I shall be out hunting every morning. The distance you've travelled, I should imagine you've seen quite enough of a horse's neck - so why don't you just stay in bed and rest? My wife will look after you.'

'I can think of nothing better,' said Gawain. But he noticed then that the lady was smiling at him rather too knowingly.

'Now,' said his host, 'since it's still the festive season, why don't we play a little game? Let's you and I make a bargain.'

'Why not?' Gawain said.

'What if I promise that I will give you whatever I bring back from the hunt?' the lord of the castle went on. 'And you promise me, in return, that you will give me anything and everything that you manage to come by back here in the castle? Well?'

'It's a bargain,' Gawain laughed. 'Anything at all I come by, you shall have, I promise - though I can't for the life of me think what it might be.'

So Gawain slept in the next morning whilst the lord of the castle went out hunting. And as he dozed, the door of his room opened silently. Gawain opened his eyes to find the lady of the castle sitting on his bed smiling down at him, her eyes full of love. Gawain didn't know which way to look, nor what to talk about - and it was very obvious that she had more in mind than just talk. But talking was all. Gawain would allow himself to do. After all, this was the wife of his kind host, his good friend. But how he was tempted! The woman was wonderfully beautiful, so beautiful he had to force himself to look away if he was to resist her. The trouble was, he didn't want to resist her, even though he knew he should.

'I am disappointed in you, Gawain,' she wheedled. 'You talk and talk, but you do not ask me to kiss you.'

'Well, if you're offering, my lady,' said Gawain, 'then who am I to turn you down?' And the lady leant over, took his face in her hands and kissed him gently.

When she had gone, Gawain got up, washed and dressed, thinking all the while of the kiss. All that day, he lazed about the castle talking happily to the lady. She made him forget all his troubles, even his encounter with the Green Knight in the Green Chapel.

At dusk the lord of the castle returned, mud-splattered from the chase. He strode into the hall and threw down a roe deer at Gawain's feet. 'Yours,' he said. 'As we agreed. What have you got for me, then?'

'This,' said Gawain, and he took his host's face in his hands and kissed him. 'That's all. I promise.'

'I believe you,' laughed the lord of the castle, 'but what I'd like to know is how you came by this kiss.'

'Oh no,' said Gawain, shamefaced. 'That wasn't part of the bargain.' And they said no more about it. That night the three of them feasted together on capons and mead, and talked and laughed into the early hours.

In the morning Gawain woke to the sound of baying hounds and hunting horns. From his bed he could see the lord of the castle riding out across the parkland. As he expected, and as he hoped too, it wasn't long before the lady came into his room. She sat on his bed, closer this time, stroked his hair and talked again of love. Gawain laughed it all off as best he could, but it was not easy. When she offered him two kisses he did not find it at all difficult to accept; and this time the kisses were sweeter and longer than before, kisses he could not forget even if he had wanted to - and he did not want to.

That evening the lord of the castle returned from the hunt, a boar slung across his shoulders. 'Here we are,' he said. 'Not a bad day's work, eh? What about you?'

'Just this,' said Gawain. And at that he kissed him twice, though not, I imagine, as long nor as sweetly as he had kissed that morning. But he had kept his part of the bargain. Dinner went on again into the small hours and through it all the lady tried to seduce him with her eyes – and with her husband there at the same table. Although Gawain tried to look the other way, he found he did not want to.

Gawain scarcely slept at all that night. Haunted by thoughts of the Green Knight, he tossed and turned. It wasn't until dawn that he sank into a troubled sleep. When he woke, the lady of the castle was gazing down at him. She had never looked more lovely, but there were tears in her eyes. 'What is it?' she cried. 'Don't you like me? Am I that ugly to you? There's someone else, isn't there? You love someone else back at Camelot.'

'No, my lady,' said Gawain, taking her hand in his. 'There's no one else. It's not that. But you have a husband, a fine man, a noble knight. He's been a good friend to me. It wouldn't be right to love you. Do you think I don't want to? As a man I want to, but as a knight I must not, I cannot. Can't you understand?'

'But why not just this once?' The lady persisted, as she stroked his hair and traced his mouth with her finger. 'No one would know. I would tell no one. You would tell no one. Where's the harm in it? Please sweet Gawain, be nice to me.'

But Gawain would have none of it. He clenched his jaw and turned away from her. 'You should go, my lady,' he said stonily. The lady bowed her head and wept.

'Like it or not, Gawain,' she said, 'you cannot stop me from loving you. I shall always keep you in my heart. I shall never forget you, never.'

'Nor I you, my lady,' Gawain said, and he meant it too.

'Will you at least do one thing for me?' she pleaded. 'Just to remind you of me from time to time, will you take this?' And she handed him the belt she wore round her waist, a belt of green ribbon interwoven with gold thread. 'Wear it always Gawain, and I promise you will never come to any harm, for there is within it an all-powerful magic. Wear it and you will be safe, wear it and think of me. I know you are not my knight and should not wear my favour, but no one need see it. One day it may save your life. Make me happy, Gawain. Do just this one little thing for me. But promise me that, whatever you do, you will never tell my husband.'

Gawain needed no persuading about that. He had no

intention of telling her husband, nor of handing over the belt either. Tomorrow he had to face the Green Knight, and this belt could be the saving of him. Now he would at least stand some chance of survival. Now he had some hope of living beyond tomorrow.

'Dear, sweet Gawain,' she whispered, and she kissed him three times, and so passionately this time that she left Gawain quite breathless, his heart pounding.

At sundown Gawain was waiting in the hall when the lord of the castle came in from the hunt, swinging a fox by its brush. Gawain went right up to him, took him by the shoulders and kissed him loudly three times. 'Three!' cried the lord of the castle, wiping his cheeks. 'And all I have to offer you in return is this poxy fox. Here, I wish you joy of it.'

Try as he might, Gawain could not enjoy the New Year's feast that night. There was wine, there was music, there was dancing. But hidden round his waist he could feel the lady's magic belt. He had not kept his promise to the lord of the castle; and worse, he knew it was out of cowardice that he had broken the bargain. The belt might save his life the next day, but it would not save his honour. All night long he lay in a turmoil of guilt, but he could not bring himself to hand over the belt and give up his only chance of life.

Gawain was up early on New Year's Day. He tied the belt round his waist, put on his warmest clothes and his fine gold-inlaid armour. Down in the courtyard he embraced his host for the last time, quite unable to look

150

him in the eye. He looked for the lady of the castle but she was nowhere to be seen. He mounted Gringolet and waved his farewells. They let down the drawbridge and, with a squire ahead to guide him, Gawain rode out into the biting January cold.

For nearly two hours they rode on, following a winding, tumbling stream along a mist-filled valley. Suddenly the squire reined in his horse and pointed. 'Over there,' he said, his voice hushed. 'Beyond those trees, you can't miss it, the Green Chapel. Sir Gawain, I know it's not my place, but if I were you I wouldn't go any closer. The Green Knight who lives there fights anyone who goes near. And I'm telling you, he never loses. Plenty have tried, but not one of them has ever lived to see another dawn. Listen, you can hear the crows gathering. Turn back Gawain, before it's too late. I won't say a word, I promise.'

'What must be done must be done,' Gawain replied. 'I am a knight of King Arthur's court. We may feel afraid, but we do not flinch and we do not run.'

'On your own head be it then,' said the squire, and he rode away and left Gawain alone in the swirling mist.

Gringolet pawed the ground, eager to be going. 'Don't be in such a hurry,' said Gawain aloud. 'I just hope and pray the lady was telling the truth about this magic belt. If not ...' And as he spoke, he heard from somewhere ahead of him a grating, grinding sound. He listened again. It was just as he feared, metal on stone. The Green Knight was sharpening his axe. Gawain shivered in spite of himself. 'What must be must be,' he sighed, and he put his spurs to Gringolet's sides, urging him onwards.

He rode through the dripping trees, crossed a stream and came to a grassy mound. Near the mound stood a small chapel the roof and walls all as green as the surrounding grass. From somewhere inside the mound itself, Gawain could hear the axe still being sharpened. It set his teeth on edge, and a shiver of fear ran down his spine. He thought of galloping off and, but for the green belt, he would undoubtedly have done so. Instead he dismounted. 'Who's there?' he shouted. 'I am Sir Gawain from King Arthur's court, and I have come as I promised I would. Come on out,'

'When I am ready,' came the reply. 'When my axe is sharp enough. I won't be long.' And the gruesome grinding ground on. He waited, pacing up and down, until at long last out came the Green Knight, feeling the blade of his axe with his thumb. He was every bit as huge and as terrifying as Gawain had remembered him. 'That will do nicely,' he said, and he looked mercilessly down at Gawain out of his grey-green, wolfish eyes. 'Welcome, Gawain,' he said.

'Let's not waste time on pleasantries,' said Gawain, longing now to have it done with. He felt his courage ebbing away with every passing moment.

'As you wish,' said the Green Knight. 'Take off your helmet, then. This won't take long.' Gawain removed his helmet, knelt down on the wet grass and bent his head. He closed his eyes and waited, but nothing happened.

'Go on then.' He could speak in no more than a whisper. 'Go on. I won't move.'

The Green Knight whirled his great axe round his head, round and round so that it whistled through the air. In spite of himself, Gawain could not stop himself from flinching.

'What's the matter with you, Gawain?' the Green Knight scoffed, leaning nonchalantly on his axe. 'We aren't frightened, are we? I thought the knights of King Arthur's court were supposed to be so brave, and I heard Sir Gawain was the bravest of all. So, the great Sir Gawain is afraid of a little whistle, is he?'.

'Get on with it, damn you,' Gawain cried. 'All right, I winced; but I won't do it again.'

'We shall see,' laughed the Green Knight. Once again he heaved up his axe. This time he held back the blow just a hair's breadth from the skin of Gawain's neck. Gawain felt the wind of it, but never moved a muscle.

'Well done, Gawain,' he said. 'That was just to see how brave you really are. This time though there'll be no holding back. Prepare yourself.'

'Can you do nothing but talk?' Gawain was more angry than frightened now. 'Strike man, strike. Or maybe you're a bit squeamish at the idea of killing a defenceless man, is that it?'

A third time now, the Green Knight swung up his axe. This time, the blade came close enough to nick the skin on Gawain's neck. Gawain felt the pain of it and the warm blood trickling down. He was on his feet in an instant, springing back and drawing his sword.

'That's it!' he cried. 'You've had your chance. One stroke, just one stroke. That was the bargain. Now I can defend myself, and by God I will.'

But strangely, the Green Knight just smiled and threw aside his axe. 'No, Gawain,' he spoke gently now, a different voice, a voice Gawain thought he knew from elsewhere. 'No, we shall not fight, you and I. We are friends. Do you not recognize me?' And as he spoke, the green of him vanished, his form changed, and he became the lord of the castle. Gawain was speechless. 'If I had wanted to, Gawain, I could easily have cut your head off, just as you did to me a year ago.'

'I don't understand any of this,' said Gawain, lowering his sword.

'You will' said the lord of the castle. 'You will. Twice I held back my axe and drew no blood. That was because you twice kept your promise to me back in the castle, first with the one kiss my wife gave you, and then with the two kisses also. I see you remember it well. But Gawain, the third time, you deceived me. Yes, I had the three kisses she gave you, but she gave you something else as well, didn't she? She gave you a favour to wear, a green belt, a magic belt with power to save your skin, so she said. You never gave it to me. You never said a word about it. And for that I cut you - though not too deep, I hope. You see, she told me everything. I knew every word that passed between you, every look. If you had once weakened, and dishonoured your knight-hood, then I can tell you, your head would be lying there at my feet, your life's blood pouring out on the grass.'

'I feel sick with shame,' said Gawain, taking off the green belt and offering it to him.

'No need, Gawain. The belt was a little thing, a little sin. No one is perfect, but you, my friend, are as close to perfect as I have ever met, or ever shall meet come to that. Keep the belt so that you do not forget us, nor what has happened here - but I'm afraid it's just an ordinary belt, it has no all-powerful magic.'

After what I did, I do not deserve such kindness,' said Gawain. 'I did you wrong. I broke my word. I dishonoured my knighthood.'

'Nonsense.' The lord of the castle took him warmly by the shoulders. 'You wished only to live. What man faced with death does not wish to live, tell me that? Come, Gawain, I've had my fill of this dank and dismal place. Let's go back to the castle and feast some more. I'm glad it's over. I tell you, I'm sick to death of green. We'll roast the boar.'

'I'm tempted,' said Gawain. 'And as you now know only too well, I've never found temptation easy to resist. But I will resist this time. I'd better be on my way home to Camelot. If I don't get back soon, they'll think I'm dead – as by rights I ought to be. But, before I go, tell me something. How were you able to turn yourself green as you did? How could you ride off with your head under your arm? And how was it that there wasn't a single drop of blood when I cut it off?'

'You deserve to know everything, and you shall,' said the lord of the castle. 'Mine is a strange story, but a true one nonetheless. My name is Sir Bernlak, Knight of the Lake. It was the Lady Nemue, the Lady of the Lake, who sent me to Camelot to test the courage of King Arthur and his knights, to find out if all the good things we had heard were true. I will tell her that there is at least one knight who is as noble as they say, and as brave and gentle too.' The two friends embraced, blessed each other and parted.

Some weeks later, Gawain came home. to Camelot. And how we feasted! After he had told us his story, he showed us the scar on his neck; and as final proof, he gave me the green belt interwoven with gold thread. He need not have done so for, knowing Gawain as we all did, none of us seated at the Round Table ever doubted a word of his story.

Notes on What Icarus Saw

Before this story begins, Pasiphae, the wife of King Minos has been made by the gods to fall in love with a bull and has given birth to a monster, half bull, half human, called the Minotaur. The monster eats only human flesh and creates constant problems for Minos, who employs Daedalus to build a maze, or labyrinth, to imprison him. Daedalus does as he is asked but later angers Minos and finds himself locked, with his son Icarus, in his own labyrinth.

What do you think?
Many people already know the story of Icarus who thinks he is invulnerable and flies too close to the sun and dies. Once we know this, the irony of the poem – where *we* know something that the narrator doesn't – is an important part of its meaning. Can you find some points in the story where this creates suspense?

Questions
1. What contrasts does the writer show between Daedalus and Icarus?

2. What do they have in common?

3. In a free verse poem like this one, the writer varies the length and rhythm of the lines to help involve us in the story. Can you find a place where you think this works especially well?

4. How would this story have been different if Daedalus told it?

5. Talk about the title and the different kinds of 'seeing' in the poem.

What Icarus Saw

The first time that he said it
I thought my dad was crazy.
(Not stupid.
No-one ever called him thick.
Weird, maybe, but not thick.)
'We might just have to fly.'

Bright man, my dad.
King Minos asked for him,
Got him to design the labyrinth,
A maze to blow your mind:
A system of a million tunnels, twined
Like tangled string, beyond
All human understanding.
Find your way out of that.

I don't know why he couldn't just stay put.
He had materials, the workshop, tools,
Run of the palace,
Endless food and drink.
Plenty of orders, jobs that he could do –
Enough for most men.
My dad wanted more,
Wanted to choose,
Be free to go.
I said
'Why not just ask the king?

You've done the maze, so
Get your pay and leave.'
He laughed a bit, and hugged me.
'You're a good lad.
But I'm afraid this kind of man
Just doesn't think that way.
He wants me, likes my work.
Why should he ever let me go?'

Well ... Make a run for it?
Crawl out one night?
Put on disguises, hobble to a boat?
We wouldn't stand a chance.
That's when he gets the big idea:
'We might just have to fly.'

I love it when he's thinking.
He hums around the workshop,
Eyes on fire, feet like a dancer's
Twinkling round the floor
Until he's got the plan:
Feathers, tons of feathers; wooden frame;
Drawings of angles, hinges, struts;
Map of the route, position of the sun;
Tureens of melting wax, to fix the wings.

How could they miss it?
All those gloomy guards
Standing on duty, plodding on patrol.

Didn't they catch the light of hope,
The burning in his eyes?
We kept the secret, locked the door
Until the time was right.

I trusted him
All the way through.
Until I stood there, on the balcony,
A ton of feathers on my back.
It was a long way down.
Knees bent, I saw the waves so far below
Crashing as breakers on the rocks
And wondered if my dad had lost his touch.

'Not down, not up.
Look straight ahead.
A steady rhythm, following wind and luck
Will take us straight to Sicily.
So, trust me, son. I'll follow.'

Off I went
Into the air.
A moment's panic
Then, a marvellous surge
A flood of confidence;
My father's wings
Could hang me in the sky
Carry me down to Africa
For I could fly.

I hear him shout
Point feebly at the sun
Like old men do
Who can't keep up.
Now now, dad. You can't hold me back.
What do you expect?
Give me my wings
And then not try them out?
You stay down there
But I am young and strong and flying
Flying free.

Way down below
He's waving, frantic,
Jabbing at the sun
Like some demented teacher
Whose blackboard message isn't getting through.

Slowly the lesson comes to me.
I feel the wax run down
Wet on my back and chest
Burning my skin.
The wings my father made
Slip off my shoulders
And I see them fall,
Poised, for a moment,
In mid air.

Notes on Little Red Riding Hood: The Wolf's Story

Here's another retelling of a well-known story from a different viewpoint. Like the next story, *The Prometheus Incident*, this one gives the traditional villain a chance to put his case.

What do you think?

The villain of the original turns into the hero/victim in this version, a man with a mission to set the record straight. What different methods does the wolf use?

Questions

1. What kind of person is Little Red Riding Hood in this version?

2. What kind of person is Granny?

3. A good retelling of a story will make us see the original through new eyes. Do you think this happens here?

4. Talk about whether you think we can still call this version a fairy story.

5. What do you think children might learn from it?

Little Red Riding Hood: The Wolf's Story

OK, so I got killed in the end and you all said yippee. I'm not complaining about that. I wasn't as clever as I thought I was, so I'll take my defeat like a wolf. But now that I'm a was-wolf (that is, a dead wolf), and I'm up here in Valhowla (paradise for wolves), I'll rest a lot easier if the record is set straight. The official accounts of what happened that day are all lies, and I hate lies – especially lies about me. So here's the story of what really happened.

The first lie that annoys me is all this big-bad-wolf business. Big? I may have been average size once, but by the time I was killed, I was more ribs than muscles. I hadn't had a decent meal in weeks. Skinny, yes – big, no. And why bad? What was ever bad about me? I reckon I'm one of the nicest wolves I know. So instead of, *In the forest there lived a big bad wolf,* now read, *In the forest there lived a skinny nice Wolf.*

Next we come to the question of motive. The history books say I wanted to eat Little Red Riding Hood. I didn't, and I can prove it. But even if I *had* wanted to eat her, what's so terrible about that? When she had eggs and bacon for breakfast, did anyone complain that big bad Red Riding Hood took the eggs from the chicken as well as two slices off Porky Pig? When she had roast turkey for Christmas, did it bother her what might have happened to Mrs Turkey and all the little Turks? When she sank her teeth into a juicy rump steak, did she spare a thought for some poor cow walking round the field with half its bottom missing? What's the difference between a little girl eating me and my mates, and me eating a little girl?

Anyway, as I said, I didn't want to eat her. Here's the proof. You remember she and I had a little chat in the woods? I asked her where she was going, what she had in the basket, and where her sick granny lived. Well, if I was close enough to talk to her, you'll have to agree that I was close enough to eat her. Why didn't I? Some of the accounts suggest it was because there were some woodcutters nearby. Rubbish. If there'd been a single woodcutter nearby, I'd have been off faster than you can say, 'The wonderful wolf went away from the wood.'

The fact is, I was after Red Riding Hood's basket with all the goodies in it. With my blunt old teeth I couldn't even bite a chicken, let alone a little girl. It was the basket I wanted. I thought of stealing it from her there and then, but for three reasons I didn't. First, I didn't want to upset her. Second, she might have started screaming, and I don't like screams, or people who hear screams. And third, she might not have let go, and I was in no condition for a fight.

My plan was very simple. I intended to pop along to Granny's cottage, give her a little scare so she'd run away for a few minutes, pretend I was Granny, and relieve Red Riding Hood of the basket. Then she would have gone home thinking she'd done her good deed, Granny would have come back feeling pleased she'd escaped from the wolf, and I'd have got the basket. We'd all have lived happily ever after.

Only things didn't quite work out that way; First of all, in spite of what the official reports might say, Granny wasn't there. I pushed open the door, all set to say 'boo' and get out of the way as she rushed out, but there was nobody to say 'boo' to. Actually, I was rather glad, because some grannies don't scare easily. I've seen grannies that scared me a good deal more than I scared them. Anyway, the room was empty, so I reckoned it was my lucky day. I crawled into bed, pulling the covers over me.

In a few minutes, Little Red Riding Hood came along, and again the history books have got it all wrong. Unless she was as short-sighted as a one-eyed rhinoceros, do you honestly think she would have taken me for her grandmother? All those lies about 'what big teeth you have', and so on. I'll tell you exactly what we said to each other.

When she knocked at the door, I stayed under the covers and called out: 'Who is it?' (That was rather clever of me. I knew who it was, but Granny wouldn't have known, would she?)

'It's me, Grandma!' said Red Riding Hood.

'Who's me?' I asked.

'You's you!' she replied.

'Well, who's you?' I asked.

'Little Red Riding Hood!' she said. 'I've brought you a basket full of lovely food.'

'Oh, surprise, surprise!' I said. 'Come in, my dear, come in.'

And in she came. Naturally, I stayed under the covers.

'How are you, Grandma?' she asked.

'I'm not well at all, dear,' I said. 'I've caught a catching illness, and as I don't want you to catch it, too, I'll stay under the covers till you've gone. Just leave the basket there, dear, and run along home. Run quickly, 'cos I've heard there's a big bad wolf in the forest.'

It was brilliant. I felt like jumping out of bed and giving myself a round of applause.

'Yes, Grandma,' said Red Riding Hood, and she put down the basket, turned round to leave, and just my luck! Who should walk into the room at that moment but Granny herself! I knew I was in trouble as soon as I heard the footsteps. I'd have made a run for it if I hadn't been paralysed with terror.

'Hullo, Red Riding Hood,' said Granny.

'Hullo, Grandma,' said Red Riding Hood.

'Hullo, trouble,' said I to myself.

'Grandma,' said Red Riding Hood, 'if you're here, who could that be in your bed?'

I wished I could just curl up and disappear down the side of the mattress.

'Whoever you are,' said Granny, 'I've got you covered. Come out with your hands up.'

I poked my nose out from under the blanket.

'Look,' I said, 'it's all been a terrible mistake …'

'It's the big bad wolf!' said Red Riding Hood.

'No, no,' I said, 'I'm just a skinny nice wolf …'

BANG, BANG, BANG!

Oh, the injustice! All I wanted was something to eat, but before I even had a chance to impress them with my charm and good intentions, Granny had put three bullets right, where I should have had the fruit cake and chocolate biscuits. I collapsed like a chopped tree.

'Good shooting, Grandma!' said Red Riding Hood – though what was good about it I shall never know.

'Quick, fetch the vet!' I gasped.

But the last thing those two had in mind was to help poor dying Wolfie.

'We ought to get the newspapers here,' said Granny. 'This could be quite a story.'

'Oh, yes,' said Red Riding Hood. 'They might publish our pictures and we'd be famous!'

And while I lay there, half in and half out of the world, they calmly discussed the tale they would tell the reporters. Granny was worried that she might get into trouble because she didn't have a licence for her gun. (I wish she'd thought of that earlier.) Red Riding Hood also wondered why Granny hadn't been in her bed, because she was supposed to be sick. It turned out that Granny had been on the lavatory, but she certainly wasn't going to tell *that* to the reporters.

'And what,' said Granny, 'are they going to think when they find the wolf in my bed? After all, I've got my reputation to think of.'

'Blow your reputation,' I groaned. 'What about me? I've been shot!'

'You keep out of this, Wolfie,' said Granny. 'You've caused enough trouble as it is.)'

I'd caused trouble! Was it my fault she'd been on the lavatory? And who fired the gun? And who didn't have a licence? But it was no use arguing – they'd made up their minds that I was the villain and they were the heroes.

'Perhaps,' said Red Riding Hood, 'we can pretend someone else shot him – a hunter, or a woodcutter.'

'But that wouldn't explain how he got into my bed,' said Granny.

'I know what,' cried Red Riding Hood. 'We could say you were in bed, and Wolfie came in and ate you.'

'You must be joking,' I moaned. 'With my teeth I couldn't even eat a chicken, let alone a tough old bird like Granny.'

'Keep quiet, Wolfie!' said Granny. 'No, the problem there, my dear, is that if he'd eaten me, I'd be dead. And I'm not.'

'Well,' said Red Riding Hood, 'we could say he ate you whole, and then the woodcutter cut him open and you came out alive.'

'Now that's an idea!' said Granny.

'Oh, yeah!' I gasped. 'A newborn fifteen-stone sixty-year-old baby! Who's going to believe that?'

'Then,' continued the Little Red Liar, 'we'll say he disguised himself as you, I came in, and the woodcutter rescued me in the nick of time.'

'Oh, well,' I groaned, 'why don't I eat a whole Red Riding Hood for dessert – make a proper meal of it?'

'Why not?' asked Granny.

'You're both crazy!' I panted. 'Nobody in this whole wide world can be stupid enough to swallow a story like that!'

Those were, my last words. With one more bullet from Granny, I huffed my last puff. But I died happy in the knowledge that nobody in the whole wide world could be stupid enough to swallow a story like that. Ugh, how wrong can a wolf be?

Notes on The Prometheus Incident

Prometheus' punishment for stealing fire (see *Pandora's Box*) was to be chained to a rock in the Caucasus Mountains and have his liver pecked out by a vulture. Each night the liver would grow again and the following day the bird would return. In this modern version, the gods who devised this punishment have put a little 'spin' on the story ...

What do you think?
To believe this official version of events we have to believe in the Chairman. What impression do you get of him?

Questions
1. Look closely at the language used in this report:
- which words and phrases help to suggest Prometheus is a criminal?
- which words and phrases play down his bravery and suffering?

2. The story is told from the gods' angle but we soon work out what's going on. How does the writer's choice of words help us to see through the Chairman's story?

3. As in the last story, this piece of writing gives the villain a chance to try to win us over. Do you react differently to the Chairman and to the wolf?

The Prometheus Incident

Annual General Meeting, Olympus plc.
THE CHAIRMAN'S REPORT.

This has been a good year for the gods. We have established control of all areas, and resistance from the Titans has been totally overcome. From our forecasts of last year, we knew that they had physical strength but little intellectual capacity, and we face the new year with no serious challenge to our power.

I should refer to one incident which has received more than its share of media attention. The Prometheus Incident, as it has become known, was treated by the human press as an adventure story. They like to build up rebel heroes, lone fighters who stand up against the crowd, and Prometheus was happy to fill the role. It may therefore be necessary to give the full facts.

Since the war, Prometheus could have suffered the same penalties as other Titans. It is true that he was sensible enough not to fight against us, but it was still our decision to spare him. We are disappointed that he could not reward this generosity with more faithful service.

We thought it kind to overlook his obsession with people. Gods also have hobbies of their own, some of which can appear curious to others. In this case, we thought the creation of men and women was harmless enough. Maybe we were at fault, and should have kept a closer eye on his activities with humans.

This strange interest not only distracted his attention from more serious matters, but also undermined his loyalty. Intelligence is the key to our affairs, and what keeps us above our competitors. We guard our secrets closely. So for Prometheus to be talking with humans, telling them the business of the gods, teaching them our skills, was bound to lead to problems.

Then there was the theft of fire. Human accounts of this incident describe an exciting chase, with Prometheus running down the hillside, sheltering the precious flame. We need now to stress that the flame was our property, which did not belong to Prometheus, and which he had no right to steal. Whether he was brave, fast or defiant makes no difference; the key fact is that he was a thief.

Human commentators who choose to ignore this fact have complained about his punishment. The weather in the Caucasus mountains is on the cold side, but it is a secluded spot, and Prometheus is therefore spared the embarrassment of public shame. He is currently chained to a pillar, which may cause some discomfort, but means that we can be certain of his whereabouts. We should not wish him to get lost while held in custody.

Animal rights campaigners are unhappy with the employment of the vulture which daily attacks his liver. We can assure them that no cruelty has been involved in the training, and that all the evidence suggests that for the vulture this is a satisfying, nutritious experience. For Prometheus it is important that he be given a clear signal. We shall not tolerate the betrayal of trust, and if his punishment also teaches others the lesson of obedience then this sad story will indeed have a happy and useful ending. And now, let us turn to the good news ...

Programme of study

WHAT MAKES A STORY LAST?

Word
Persephone in Hell
1. Read through the description of Demeter cursing Ascalaphus, from 'She raised her hand ...' to '... in the midst of joy.' (p.17). Pick out three separate words which you think describe well what's going on, because they give us a clear picture or feeling.

The Fight with Grendel
2. In this poem the sound of words is part of what they mean – to get the feel of it you need to read it aloud. Look at two examples in the first few lines:
- line 4: 'buffet', a word that feels like a collision, and suggests a battering fight.
- line 9: 'lurked' describes someone hiding, but it also sounds sinister and sneaky, a dark sort of word.

   Now look at the description of Beowulf's fight with Grendel, from 'over the misty moor ...' to the end. Pick three words where you think the sound echoes the meaning, and for each one try to explain the feeling it gives you.

3. 'The hall of Heorot rang loud and long
With woe of warriors and grief of the great king.'

   In these two lines there are four examples of *alliteration*, words chosen because they start with the same letter, and seem to echo each other:
- hall ... Heorot
- loud ... long
- woe ... warriors
- grief ... great

The sounds here suggest the size and depth of the sadness, particularly the long 'o' sound in 'woe'. Find two other examples of alliteration in the poem, and comment on the feelings they are trying to suggest.

Sentence
The Princess in the Suit of Leather

4. Look carefully at the first sentence, and the last sentence, of the story. What do you think the teller is trying to do in each of these sentences (not necessarily the same for each one) and what do you notice about each sentence which is unusual?

The Invisible One
5. In a story that's meant to be told aloud, the pattern of the sentence often makes it easier for the listener to follow. Look at these two examples, and the comments on them.

Sentence: 'Therefore there were indeed few who did not make the trial, but it was long ere one succeeded.'

Comment: This sentence is split in two halves, with a contrast between many attempting it, but only one succeeding.

Sentence: 'In saying which they lied, like the rest, for they had seen nothing and got nothing for their pains.'

Comment: The two sisters are just like many other competitors, and so their deceit gets its just reward in the end – see nothing, get nothing.

Now provide your own comment on this sentence:
'Now this poor small wretch in her mad attire, with her hair singed off and her little face as full of burns and scars as there are holes in a sieve, was for all this, most kindly received by the sister of the Invisible One, for this noble girl knew more than the mere outside of things as the world knows them.'

Then choose for yourself one more sentence from this story, and provide your own comment on how it is organised.

Text

Persephone in Hell

6. The key events of this story take place in five conversations:
- Demeter pleading with Zeus
- Hermes asking Hades to free Persephone
- Hades feeling sad, but agreeing
- Demeter cursing Ascalaphus
- Demeter telling Rhea about her sadness.

But in between these, there are detailed descriptions of Hermes' journey down to Hades, of Persephone, and so on. Pick two examples of these descriptions, comment on how they work and the feelings they suggest, and say how they help the story.

The Princess in a Suit of Leather

7. This is a complicated story, which weaves together four strands:
- The king's grief for his wife, and then for his daughter
- The attempts of his court to solve his problem
- The princess's escape from the king
- The princess and the prince, and their courtship.

Describe how the story moves between these four, and how they are brought together at the end.

WHAT DOES A STORY MEAN?

Word

The Wicked King and his Good Son

8. This story is a portrait of a selfish, proud man. Pick out four different words, from different points of the story, which describe how the king talks and behaves.

God's Footprints

9. One important point about this story is the view we get of God. He is not the distant, serious characters you might meet in many religious books, but down to earth and almost human. Pick three words used about him in the story, which help us to think of God as ordinary.

Sentence

The Wicked King and his Good Son

10. Look at the paragraph beginning 'That, as far as King Hiranya Kashyap was concerned …'. There are three sentences, which all follow this pattern:
'If A …, then B …'

Comment on each of the sentences, and on the difference between the first part and the second. Then look at how the sentences build up from the start of the paragraph to the end, and comment on how they change.

God's Footprints

11. Notice how the writer uses rhyme in this sentence, to build up a clumsy rhythm, as God blunders around:

'God tumbled out of bed, fumbled his feet into his sandals and stumbled out of doors into the first light of morning.'

Write your own sentences, each of which should include three words that rhyme, to describe the following:
- a footballer scoring a goal
- a wild animal attacking its prey
- a peaceful peace of music.

Text

The Wicked King and his Good Son

This story tells what happens between Hiranya and Prahlad, but it is also held together by the way in which the start of the story is linked with the way it finishes.

12. Look closely at the first paragraph and explain how the storyteller ties it up with the ending of the story. How does this work on the page? How would it work it it were being told aloud?

Deer Hunter and White Corn Maiden
13. As we follow a story, we guess what's coming next. Sometimes we guess wrongly, or the story makes us expect one thing, and then gives us another.

When we first hear about Deer Hunter and Corn Maiden, we expect that they'll get married and live happily ever after. Then Corn Maiden is ill, and maybe we expect her to recover …

Go through the stages of this story, saying each time what you expected to happen, and what actually happened.

John Barleycorn
14. In a regular poem like this, the stanzas (or verses) work like paragraphs, dividing the story up into stages. But they also look similar, and often relate to each other, inviting us to see a pattern in how they are contrasted with each other, or in bits they repeat.

What kinds of pattern can you see in the stanzas of this poem?

THE WAY YOU TELL THEM

Word
Balder
15. 'Frigga had twin boys, and they were as different as it was possible for two boys to be.'

Make two columns, headed HODUR and BALDER, and collect at least four words which are used to describe each of them. Is there any pattern in the words that are used?

The Death of Gelert

16. This is a poem which tells an old, dramatic story. Pick three words from the poem which suggest that this happened a long time ago, and three words which help to put across the sense of violence.

Sentence

Balder

17. 'In the cold, mountain country of the North, that we now call Scandinavia, Asgard was the kingdom of the gods.'

'She had a palace of her own, and a mind of her own, and, when she needed to be, could be cleverer than the king.'

Many of the sentences in this story have their own pattern, like the rhythms of a poem. It depends on the grouping of phrases, the punctuation, stressed and unstressed syllables, and the sounds of words.

Write your own final paragraph (of at least four sentences) for a story like this, set in Asgard, describing the end of the world.

Pandora's Box

18. Look at the sentence on p.134 which begins 'At that moment, all the things that make life difficult …'.

This is much longer than any other sentence in the story. Normally, a big, long list like this would just be boring, and we'd cut it, or divide it up into shorter sentences.

Look carefully at the way the whole story finishes, and then write about how this sentence works, and what it contributes to the ending of the story.

Text
Under Ben Bulben
19. When stories are told aloud, it helps the teller and the listener to have a pattern. Often – but not always – things come in threes. For instance, at the end of 'Under Ben Bulben', Finn has three chances to save the dying Dermot. If he thought he would help but then changed his mind, three times in succession, that would just be dull. Describe what happens each time Finn has a chance to save Dermot.

The Poor Man's Reward
20. This is a story where the poor man wins the princess, after passing several tests. It's also a story where a man helps some creatures, without realising that they will end up helping him.

Make a list of each creature, with what he does for them and what they do for him. What do you notice about the number of creatures, and the order in which they return his favours?

The Death of Gelert
21. Stanzas, or verses, divide up a poem. In a ballad like this, they can help you to tell the story quickly. At stanza 14, for instance, a prose story might start 'When he realised what he had done, Llewellyn felt guilty, and spoke to the dead body of his faithful dog "Oh, Gelert …" '. The poem doesn't need that. It gets straight on with the story, jumping from the body to the grief. The rhythm carries the reader forward, and we work out Llewellyn's feelings for ourselves.

You might imagine it as a comic strip, with each stanza taking you a stage further in the story. Write a caption for each of the stanzas 9–15, summing up the main thing that happens in that verse (maximum: eight words for each box).

The Mind of Anansi

22. This is another story poem where the rhythm drives you forward, but this time it goes in couplets, from rhyme to rhyme. It's like a rap, with a smooth-talking narrator telling the story, acting the parts, and enjoying the fact that sometimes it sounds as if it's hard to make it rhyme.

Pick out three couplets (pairs of rhyming lines) where you think the rhymes work really well – because they're neat, or unexpected, or funny, or dramatic, or for any other reason of your own.

TELL ME THAT AGAIN

Word
Sir Gawain and the Green Knight

23. Read the passage describing the preparations for the fight on pp. 150–152. 'Gawain was up early ... out of his grey-green, wolfish eyes.'

Pick out five separate words from the description which suggest movement, appeal to the senses, or give you a strong feeling of what's happening.

What Icarus Saw

24. (Not stupid.
No-one ever called him thick.
Weird, maybe, but not thick.)'

Icarus is careful about the words he uses. Pick three words from the poem which help to give us a clear picture of Icarus' dad, and say what picture or feeling each word puts across.

Little Red Riding Hood: The Wolf's Story

25. 'But now that I'm a was-wolf (that is a dead wolf), and I'm up here in Valhowla (paradise for wolves), I'll rest a lot easier if the record is set straight.'

Here the wolf is making up his own language, inventing special words for wolves – 'was-wolf' and 'Valhowla' (rather than Valhalla).

Write the first paragraph of a story from the point of view of a cockroach, a cat or an elephant. You must include at least three words which you've made up specially.

Sentence

Little Red Riding Hood: The Wolf's Story

26. 'OK, so I got killed in the end and you all said yippee.'

This is a good, short lively start to the story. By the time we have read that first sentence, how many things do we know?

The Prometheus Incident

27. This describes a passionate, violent story in the language of a company report (formal, public, looking at business benefits but without feeling). The same story could be told in a very different way.

Pick three separate sentences from this story, not necessarily close together, and rewrite them as follows:
- one as it might be in a story for young children
- one as it might be in a sentimental romantic novel
- one as it might be in a horror comic.

Text

Sir Gawain and the Green Knight

28. Ideas can hold a story together. One key idea in this story is the promise. When you make it, you should keep it, but what happens when two promises collide?

(a) Trace the promises made in this story:
- between Gawain and the lord of the castle – and what happens each time
- between Gawain and the lady of the castle.

(b) What happens when Gawain learns the truth? Who else in this story offers to make a promise?

Little Red Riding Hood: The Wolf's Story

29. 'So, here's the story of what really happened …'. This is about putting the story straight. It's a nice twist as a way of starting, but to make it work you have to keep thinking of new ideas, ways in which the traditional tale got it wrong.

Try to find up to ten changes that the wolf makes to the usual story.

Glossary

beheld: saw
bier: coffin carrier
bounteous: generous
calabash: fruit skin used for carrying
capering: dancing
celestial: heavenly
clad: dressed
consummated: done, carried out
coquettish: flirty
delectable: delicious, tasty
demur: disagree, make trouble
desecrate: spoil
desolately: sadly
dhoti: loin-cloth
disdainful: scornful
encompassed: held
epic: long heroic poem
ere: before
favour: part of a lady's clothing, worn by a knight in battle
fell: terrible
fiend: the devil
geometry: a type of maths
gourd: large fruit, dried and used as container
half-gorged: half-full
impetuous: rash
inauspicious: unhopeful
invincible: cannot be beaten
langorously: lazily
lamenting: wailing
laurels: past successes
lustreless: dull

malignant: evil
mediator: go-between
misbegotten: illegitimate, deformed
motley: varied
passed in this wise: happened like this
peer: equal
proof: protected
pyre: funeral fire
quadi: secretary
quod: prison
ravenous: hungry
rudiments: basics
runes: old marks with meanings
a score: twenty
seraglio: part of the palace
severed: cut off
sorghum: cereal crop
strove: tried
succulent: juicy
touche: we're equal now
trait: characteristic, personal quality
trident: three-pronged spear
tureen: large cooking pot
turmoil: confusion
unslaked: unsatisfied
vagaries: unexpected happenings
wadi: dry valley
wampum: shell beads used as money
wazir: minister
wonted: usual
wrought: made:
yams: plants eaten in Africa

Notes

What Makes a Story Last?
Persephone in Hell
As with other myths, names can make it complicated. Not only are there Greek and Roman versions (Prosperina and Persephone etc), but there are different names within the Greek versions – like Core and Persephone. We've gone for simplicity, to make it easier for pupils to follow, but feel free to sketch out the full background if you wish.

The Fight with Grendel
We've chosen the Serraillier version, as being lively and accessible. The Seamus Heaney version could make an interesting comparison. There's also useful potential, whether or not through comparison, in a look at how the story sounds – alliteration, onomatopoeia and so on.

The Princess in the Suit of Leather
There's an interesting point here about traditional patriarchal societies, and how stories can offer women to a freedom of choice and action that many of them are denied in everyday life.

The Invisible One
There's a clear connection with the Cinderella story but it's also an interesting teaching point: do you point this out, or wait for pupils to discover it for themselves?

There are many examples of stories we think of as 'ours', only to find them turning up, with minor variations, in other countries. For English children Cinderella is a pantomime story; adults might also know the story as 'Cendrillon' in Charles Perrault's eighteenth century fairytale collection; some Scottish children will know it as

'Rashin Coatie', a tale told in Morayshire of an ill-treated younger daughter who makes herself a dress from rushes.

The real surprise is to find it turning up in several North American Indian tribes, as 'The Rough-Faced Girl', but it began its North American life as 'The Invisible One'. Once it had crossed the Atlantic, probably carried by French fur traders, it was adapted to include elements of Indian culture and religion.

In the original version there is a cry of 'Alajulaa' at the end of the story, and the Mi'kmaq web page suggests this may have been put in, tongue in cheek, to please to please the Baptist missionary to whom she is telling the tale. The missionary then includes it in her own collected version, a nice example of how tellers adapt tales (see p.42).

What are Friends For?
How difficult this collection is for pupils will depend very much on the pattern of the work – whether or not the teacher reads stories aloud, how much is done in groups, and so on. But for pupils with limited confidence or ability in reading, this is a story they should be able to tackle alone.

What Does a Story Mean?
The Wicked King and his Good Son
The Christian tradition has tended to establish an idea of god as omnipotent, monolithic and rather dull. One value of mixing different cultures is to establish a plurality of gods, often with distressingly human characteristics. Whether or not it's accurate theology, it makes for more narrative variety and excitement.

There's also a good example of prophecy that lies like truth ('you cannot be killed by man, beast or weapons …') which will be familiar to students of *Macbeth*.

Whose Footprints?

The comment about varied gods also applies here, where the main characters of god and servant are clearly distinguished, almost in competition. It's a subtle balance, where they manage to combine their different qualities and motives in an effective working relationship.

Deer Hunter and White Corn Maiden

One reason for including this story is for its surprise value. Whatever their circumstances at home, children watching romantic films learn that boy meets girl, and when they go off together that's a happy ending. This story suggests that that ain't necessarily so, and one useful strategy to underline its surprising nature might be to read it aloud, and stop at key points to ask pupils what they think will happen next.

John Barleycorn

This version is by a Scottish poet, although the story also appears as an English folksong and as a comic tale about American drunks.

How Coyote Stole Fire

It's a lovely indication of the range that stories can cover, that the same small tale – encountered in a children's book – can both evoke memories of Prometheus and explain the markings on a squirrel.

The Way You Tell Them

Under Ben Bulben

Irish readers will be appalled at our rendering of Diarmidh and Grainne, but we've gone for maximum ease of reading among the majority of the UK readership. Nothing impedes a story more than 'How do you pronounce that?' so if you can supply more Celtic authenticity, please do, and forgive us.

Poor Man's Reward
In this section, this story serves a useful double purpose – the importance of pattern, and the surprise that it deals with a sequence of four rather than three. That shouldn't detract from its powerful links with Cinderella stories.

Balder
Prose rhythm is notoriously hard to analyse, but you can't miss it when it's there. Our guess is that pupils have more chance of responding to this element through imitation than through formal analysis – but by all means try that if you disagree.

Again, there are links with Persephone and it's interesting to see the varieties of tone within these 'cycle' stories. Sometimes there's a good news/bad news balance, the sense of a reasonable deal. This version is much more black, of a pure ideal of spring growth, lost for good.

The Death of Gelert
Visitors to Snowdonia will know the small town of Beddgelert (which means 'Gelert's Grave') and may well have seen the monument recording this story.

Ballads are fun to teach, and fun to write, but you can get dire results. The key is not to rush into rhymes too quickly. Get the outline of the story fixed; then collect relevant rhyme words, chosen from the story, and patterns of rhymes – maybe in groups. Only then do you move to writing lines, and keep them at least as long as these (so there's room to adapt the sense to accommodate the rhyme).

The Mind of Anansi
We've tried to vary the geographical sources for these stories, although we are more familiar with North America and Europe than with Latin America or the East. This is our only Caribbean

representative, but that may be a deficiency your class can remedy. (As with other geográphical regions, this is an area where the benefits of multi-cultural backgrounds should be rapidly apparent). Anansi is also a close relative of Trickster and the English Puck.

Pandora's Box
There's a lot of good writing done with lists. One variant on this might be to get pupils to do their own nightmare collections, with original contemporary details – opening up a school locker, say, or a government minister's despatch box; the ingredients of the pizza box from hell ... enjoy.

Tell Me That Again
Sir Gawain and the Green Knight
We thought about including an extract from the original, and decided against. You may disagree, but in any case this is a good, lively telling of a famous story – and it also satisfies 'Arthurian' demands from the National Curriculum.

What Icarus Saw
This is a useful simple model of irony in action – as readers we know things that the narrator doesn't understand (as the title underlines). A further exploration might be away from the Daedalus story, into other examples of partial or faulty narration.

Little Red Riding Hood: The Wolf's Story
The private eye tone is unexpected and fun, and could well provoke similar departures in different directions – westerns? contemporary soap? sci-fi?

The Prometheus Incident
The company report is a deliberately alien form – no, of course you don't want lots of company reports. But you could open up the

'form' debate, by inviting a wider range of contributions – graffiti, exchange of e-mails, love letter, school report.

Assignments

Here are some extra ideas for assignments, exploring the links between stories and encouraging pupils to use them as a basis for further creative work in a variety of media.

What Makes a Story Last?

1. *Settings*

These are not just any old stories. They happen in special places, important times - sometimes before the beginning of time. Share out the stories in this section between the members of your group, and make a list of the time and place in which each story happens.

Then work out your own group story, which starts with one the following phrases:

- 'Before the planets were ...'
- 'Above the roof of the sky ...'
- 'On the edge of the dark, is a ...'.

2. *What Happens?*

Stories deal with events, things happening, in order. The main events in the extract from *Beowulf* are:

- distant news of Grendel
- Grendel arrives
- Beowulf fights Grendel
- Beowulf kills Grendel.

Make your own lists of events like this, for two of the other stories, using eight lines or less for each story.

3. *Events in order*

A comic strip has to divide up the events of a story, to tell it a box at a time. Write and draw your own comic strip, of six boxes, to tell the important part of one of the stories in this section.

4. *Acting Monsters*

Drama is a good way to put across what makes us afraid. Films use special effects, lighting and music, but it's quite possible to do it just with people, movements and sound.

- Use a group to make a monster, and make it frightening. How will you arrange the people? How will it move? What noise(s) will it make?
- Think about people's reactions. How can you create a monster, without the monster being there - just by using the way people talk, point, look? Build up a scene in which a monster is heard about, comes closer, and then attacks - but the monster is not actually acted by anyone.
- Act out one of the famous monster stories - e.g. *Jack and the Beanstalk*, *David and Goliath*, *Theseus and the Minotaur*, *Odysseus and Cyclops*.

5. *Looking for a Hero*

In your group, go through the stories in this section, making a list of the different hero figures, and finding three character words for each of them (e.g. clever, attractive, determined …). Then create your own advertising campaign, looking for the ideal hero for the twenty-first century. You will need posters and a TV advert, and you should prepare at least one job interview in which a possible candidate applies for the job.

6. *Heroines in Action*

Most old stories have male heroes, because for a long time many people thought that only men could be heroes. Or, maybe it was because it was men that told the stories. Women were there to be admired or rescued, but they didn't do much.

Nowadays, we want female heroes who act and think for themselves. In mixed groups, work out play scenes which show a modern, female hero in action. (Should we say 'heroine' or 'female hero'? What do you think is the difference?)

7. *Why Did this Story Last?*
In your group, read and talk about one story, and then prepare a group presentation. This must involve all the members of your group, and must include the following:
- a short summary of the story
- an extract from the story - one of the best bits
- why you think this story has lasted
- what you thought of it.

8. *Modern Cinderella*
The Invisible One is a version of the Cinderella story, but it has been changed, to suit the people who would hear the story. Write your own Cinderella story, for one of the following:
- children on a housing estate
- a travelling performance in India
- a Disney film
- a rap version, in New York.

9. *What's the Story?*
Make up your own story, using four of these characters:
- the wise old magician
- the wicked witch
- the foolish farmhand
- the lonely king
- the loving mother
- the proud princess
- the faithful servant.

Before you start to write the story, write down the setting (time and place), the main characters (give them names) and a list of events (things that happen).

What Does a Story Mean?

10. *Telling in groups.*

    (a) Each group prepares to tell a particular story aloud. They can read the story now, and help each other, but when the time to perform it comes they can only have eight lines of notes to help them (see exercise 2 on p. 195). Each member of the group will be performing, so you need to know how you're going to tell it, and what you think it means. (You can use the introduction to help you, but don't just repeat it. Try to go into more detail, look more closely at your story.)

    (b) New groups are formed, each one containing someone who has prepared a different story. In turn, each person tells the story they have prepared. After each telling, each member of the group should ask a question, about some part of the story or what it might mean.

    (c) On your own now, write about 'The Meaning of Stories'. You should deal with the story you told and what it might mean, and two of the other stories you have heard. You should also say what you thought and felt about each of the stories.

11. *How Should We Behave?*

In groups, look at as many stories as you can for suggestions about how we should behave. Look at such things as:

- lovers
- children and parents
- citizens
- people and gods.

Which things in the stories do you agree with? Which things do you disagree with?

12. *'You See that Mountain?'*
Stories were often used to explain how rivers were formed, or why a hill was a particular shape. Write your own story about a piece of landscape (which can be real or imaginary) and how it came to be the way it is. Add pictures, maps or diagrams if they help to make it clear.

13. *'But it's Different Now Isn't It?'*
These stories go back a long time, and in some ways they seem part of an old way of life – simple farming, no technology. But in some ways they're very up to date.

Choose one of these stories, and write your own twenty-first century version, which changes the details but shows how the main ideas are still true.

14. *'… And That's Why People Die.'*
This is the last line of a story which is told to explain why people have to die. It's your job to make up the rest of the story.

15. *'That's Not How I Read It.'*
In your reading of this section, have you found a story about which people could disagree, and argue about its meaning? On your own, or with a partner, write your own dialogue in which two characters disagree about a story, the people in it and what it means. (You might have to make this up, and agree to disagree; even if in real life you both think the same, try to imagine two people who read the same story and come up with different ideas.)

The Way You Tell Them

16. *Tips for Telling Tales*

Your group's job is to write a leaflet about how to tell stories. You're going to give ten suggestions to storytellers, about how to tell a good story. You can use your own ideas and opinions, and you should also use quotes from three of the stories in this section – but you can't use any of the examples used in the introduction.

17. *Starting the Story*

At the beginning of a story, you have lots of choices. How are you going to start? With a person or a place. An action or an idea? *Under Ben Bulben* could have started like this:

'When an active man gains in weight and loses his hair …'
Or like this:

'Ben Bulben is a mountain like a table. It rises …'
Or like this:

'At the top of the stairs Finn MacCool stopped, to pause for breath.'

Would any of these be better than the way the story starts? If so, why?

Now try to write your own alternative beginnings, for one or more of the stories in this section.

18. *Get the Rhythm*

Practise using rhythm for telling a story, by telling the same story in different ways. You are going to write the first eight lines of one of the following stories:

- *Theseus and the Minotaur*
- *Aladdin*
- *Icarus and Daedalus*
- *Little Red Riding Hood*,

but you're going to write them out three times:

199

- in a prose version, sounding as grand and powerful as you can (like *Balder*)
- in a fast-moving ballad, with rhymes and four-line verses (like *Gelert*)
- in lively rhyming couplets (like *The Mind of Anansi*).

19. *Story Circles*

Prepare to tell your own made-up story (without any notes on paper), which must include:
- an opening to grab the listener's attention
- a pattern of three
- a moment of suspense
- an ending that people will remember.

In groups of five or six, tell your story in turn.
(You might, in new groups, pass on the best story that you've just heard - or feed back reaction to the rest of the class.)

20. *Using the group*

A storyteller has lots of things they can use - their voice, their hands, the way they move and look. In a group you have different people, different voices, ways of standing and moving together. It could be a play, or a chant, or a group reading, or a mime or a mixture of these. In a group, plan how you could together tell one of the stories in this section.

Tell Me That Again

21. *Seeing Both Sides*

In pairs, prepare an argument between two people, about one of the stories in this section. One person has just read a modern retelling, and tries to explain what's good about it. Both people in the argument need to know the story well, and refer to it.

22. *What Daedalus Knew*

What Icarus Saw was limited, because he was young and impatient, and he didn't understand everything that was going on. (And he also died before Daedalus got home.)

Using the events in the poem, write your new version, from the father's point of view, called 'What Daedalus Knew'. Don't just think about what happens. Think how he would describe it, and how he would feel.

23. *Twisting the Tale*

You can retell a story so as to change it completely - like *Little Red Riding Hood: The Wolf's Tale*. Pick a well-known children's story and do a modern version, which completely changes it:

- *Cinderella*
- *Goldilocks*
- *Beauty and the Beast*
- *Rapunzel*.

24. *It Doesn't Have to Be a Story*

Many versions of stories in this book are poems. But there are also other ways of retelling a story, without using the story form. The *Prometheus Incident*, for instance, uses the form of a chairman's report at a business meeting. There are other forms you might use, like:

- letters
- a diary
- TV documentary
- radio interview.

Pick one of these, and use it to retell one of the stories in this book.

25. *Changing Stories*

Write an essay called 'Changing the Story' which deals with at least two of the stories in this section. In each case, write about:

- the original story
- which part of it has been chosen, and if/how it's been changed
- the storyteller, and their tone and rhythm
- their attitude to the story
- your own reaction.

26. *Do it Yourself*

Pick one of the stories from another section of this book, and do your own re-written version, from a different point of view. Think about who you will be (as the storyteller), what you will keep and what you will change.

Acknowledgements

We are grateful to the following for permission to reproduce copyright material:

The author's agent for the story "The Princess in the Suit of Leather" by Angela Carter from *The Virago Book of Fairy Tales* © The Estate of Angela Carter 1990; Faber and Faber Limited for the story "How Coyote Stole Fire" by V. Haurland from *Faber Book of North American Legends*; the author Paul Francis for his stories "The Death of Gelert" © Paul Francis 2002, and "What Icarus Saw" © Paul Francis 2002; Liberty Books for the stories "The Prometheus Incident" by R. Nowell from *Myths at Work*, and "Under Ben Bulben" by N F Paul from *How Myths Work*; Macmillan Children's Books Limited for the story "Little Red Riding Hood" by David Henry Wilson from *There's a Wolf in my Pudding*; Orion Children's Books for the stories "Anansi and the Mind of God" and "Whose Footprints?" by Geraldine McGaughrean from *The Golden Hoard*; Penguin Books Limited for the stories "Persephone in Hell" by L. Garfield and E. Blishen from *The God beneath the Sea*, and "The Wicked King and His Good Son" by M. Jaffrey from *Seasons of Splendour*; and Anne Serraillier for the poem "The Fight with Grendel" by Ian Serraillier from *Beowulf the Warrior*.

In some instances we have been unable to trace the owners of copyright material and we would appreciate any information that would enable us to do so.